To Doc
with

December 2005

A BRIEF HISTORY
OF PSYCHIATRY

J. W. MALTBY

HALSGROVE

First published in Great Britain in 2005

British Library Cataloguing-in-Publication Data
A CIP record for this title is available from the British Library

ISBN 1 84114 487 8

HALSGROVE

Halsgrove House
Lower Moor Way
Tiverton, Devon EX16 6SS
Tel: 01884 243242
Fax: 01884 243325
email sales@halsgrove.com
website www.halsgrove.com

*Cover illustrations: Main picture: 'Empathy - A little fellow feeling in the bosom' - depicts
Cupid touching the breast of Venus who is enamoured of Mars (seated left), while her
husband Vulcan (the blacksmith) works on an armoured helmet.* Courtesy Christies, London.
*Inset images - from left to right: Dean Swift, Jean-Marie Charcot, Philippe Pinel,
William Battie, Alfred Adler, Sigmund Freud, Carl Jung, Eugen Bleuler.*

Printed and bound in Great Britain by
The Cromwell Press, Trowbridge

CONTENTS

FRONTISPIECE

'The Sadness of Adam and Eve'

'The Angel driving Adam and Eve from the Garden of Eden'
Michael Burghers (c.1653–1727)

Some Natural Tears they dropped. But wiped them soon
The World was all before them – where to choose...
(John Milton – Paradise Lost.)

PROLOGUE

Primum non nocere – First, do no harm.

Some people kill themselves quickly, with a rope. Others slowly, with alcohol or heroin.

Some people sell their sexuality, others (especially children) have it stolen. Yet others throw it away, to their infinite regret, later.

Some people are driven mad, others just go mad.

Madness has been defined as loss of touch with reality. But what is reality? If it is other people then it is loss of touch with other people – in a word – alienation. In the 19th century what we would now call psychiatrists were called alienists. The alienated are now called psychotic.

Every new 'diagnosis' represents a new licensing opportunity.

I believe that self-analysis is often a mistake, and leads one down endless and unprofitable paths of speculation. (Jan Morris)

Happiness is like a butterfly, the harder you chase it, the more it eludes you. Only sit quietly and it will come to rest on your shoulder (old proverb).

Q. How many psychiatrists does it take to change a light bulb? A. Only one, but it has got to want to be changed.

Psychotherapy is the process whereby the bland teach the unbland to be bland.

A neurotic – builds castles in the air. A psychotic – lives in them A psychiatrist – collects the rent.

5

A BRIEF HISTORY OF PSYCHIATRY

There are physicians for the body and physicians for the soul, but they are not two, but one.

What we need are more kindly friends and fewer professionals. (Masson)

Humour is reason's greatest ally.

A historian's understanding of the past and of the motives of the people who make history is bound to be influenced by his own experience and his capacity to understand human beings. This is why neither history nor psycho-analysis can be assigned to the exact sciences.
(Anthony Storr)

Personal names included in the index are in **bold** where they first occur in the text. The Subject Index includes general terms that appear as sub-headings or are shown in *italics* where they first occur within the text.

DEDICATION

This book is dedicated to the memory of my sister, Anne, who suffered many things of many physicians; in the hope that her life, her death, was not entirely in vain.

GLOSSARY

'Incorrect use of words leads to confusion of thought.'

Affect
>	Psychiatrist's term meaning emotion. The affective disorders include mania and depression.

Alcoholic
>	A patient whose alcohol consumption is marginally greater than that of his physician. 'Ashes to Ashes, Dust to Dust, if the Women don't get you, the Liquor must.'

Alcoholics Anonymous
>	In 1931 **Carl Jung** saw an American patient Roland H., for treatment of his alcoholism. After several weeks, or possibly months, Jung's therapy was unsuccessful in stopping his binge drinking. He was advised to seek alternative treatment, and Jung suggested he join the Oxford Group (Moral Rearmament) , which conducted its meetings through strict ritualistic procedures in the hope that such a structure might lead to a conversion experience of a religious or spiritual nature that would give him the strength to stop drinking, which it did. Back in the States, he told his friend Bill W. another hopeless alcoholic, what had happened, and together they founded AA. There is no social hierarchy, no money is exchanged, and long standing feelings that have been blocked from consciousness are revealed and hopefully dealt with so that the patient can get on with his or her life – classical Group Therapy

Alcoholism
>	A chronic relapsing condition. See under Chap 2 diagnosis.

Amnesia
>	Forgetfulness. May be 'organic', due to pathological changes in the brain, characterised typically by loss of memory for recent events, or 'functional' meaning dysfunctional, a dissociation usually due to intense anxiety. After a severe head injury involving loss of consciousness, there may be periods of amnesia, pre-traumatic or post

7

traumatic indicating the severity of the damage. Often the memory progressively recovers but there always remains a deficit.

Functional amnesia is an emergency defence mechanism that shields against overwhelming anxiety, often 'global'- forgetting one's identity. A case is described of an elderly man with complete amnesia who agreed to undergo conscious sedation. A slow intra- venous drip of diazepam was set up over 90 minutes and his memo- ry recovered. He recalled that he had left home after 'considerable marital discord'. 'He now lives alone with no memory problems.' (BMJ Vol 327 p.570 6.9.03).

In the past barbiturates have been used, particularly to treat mutism, hence the name 'truth drug'. Also used by 'intelligence' agencies.

Belief

A belief is a working hypothesis, ideas held with varying degrees of conviction, at an intellectual as well as an emotional level.

Brain Washing

A technique developed by the Russians under Stalin, amongst others, to de-personalize an individual. By imprisoning a person in a cell and depriving him of all human contact and altering the awareness of day and night, it was found possible to reduce someone to total ignorance of their previous existence. The equivalent of 'stripping' the hard disc of a computer. One of best known victims of this form of torture was Cardinal Mindzenti, the Catholic Primate of Hungary, who was forced to deny his faith.

Catatonia/catatonic

A condition regarded as a variety of schizophrenia in which the patient becomes totally rigid and unresponsive. A patient is described in which, previously active and talkative, suddenly passed into a mute state, standing like a statue for long periods. It would suddenly remit, and suddenly recur. The Norwegian psychiatrist **R.A.Gjessing** found that during stupor, more nitrogen was excreted than swal- lowed. He knew that thyroxine caused catabolism, and, although there was no evidence of thyroid disturbance, he gave the patient thy- roxine, and the periodic catatonia disappeared and stayed away so long as the thyroid was administered. Nowadays, catatonia would be treated with chlorpromazine. But this does suggest that there may be some endocrine imbalance in the pathogenesis of schizophrenia. A condition similar to catatonia is *flexibilitas cerea*, in which the limbs retain any position in which they are placed.

Celibacy
Abstention from marriage.

Chastity
Abstention from sexual intercourse

Cognitive – (Lat- *cognoscere – to know*)
The intellectual as opposed to the emotional or instinctive aspect of the personality. Especially Verbal, Literate and Numerate aspects. In Cognitive Behaviour Therapy it means thinking as opposed to knowing. In connection with Alzheimer's disease, 'loss of cognitive function' mean 'memory loss', particularly for recent events.

Confrontation
Verbal abuse by therapists is an easy outlet for their feelings of aggression towards their patients, leading to feelings of terror and powerlessness in the patients. It is totally counter-productive and should never be tolerated.

Déjà vu
An illusion in which the situation is incorrectly perceived as a repetition of a previous experience.

Delusion
A delusion is an erroneous belief, held with absolute conviction, mainly at an emotional level. Treatment is difficult. Ideas in general cannot be altered by medication. However the response to the ideas can. A person may sincerely believe he is Napoleon (Delusion of Grandeur) but is harmless enough provided he keeps his ideas to himself and does not try to raise an army to defeat the Russians or the English.

There are some religions who assert life after death, and suicide by bombing is encouraged, causing appalling damage, death and destruction and terrible grief in the survivors.

Depression
See under Diagnosis – Chapter 2

Dissociation

A loss of access to specific memory data that seem to hold some degree of emotional significance, causing amnesia. (**Pierre Janet**). He believed that they could be reconnected under hypnosis. Freud thought that psychotherapy was necessary. Probably caused by acute anxiety. Murderers sometimes dissociate.

Domain

Every living thing occupies a 'space' In the case of mankind, it is a piece of land on which a dwelling is built, and he or she occupies that space. Primitive tribes believe a person belongs to the land, the more sophisticated believe that the land belongs to them. Herein lies a conflict. As well as occupying physical space, an individual has a non-physical element – psychological space – his or her parents, children, relatives, friends, partners (both sorts) and associates. It is crucially important to investigate this because in it may lie the cause of the patient's breakdown, and a clue to their recovery. Loss of this space causes acute anxiety and depression.

Eclectic

The method or practice of selecting what seems to be best from various systems. Many psychiatrists say they are eclectic meaning that no one theory or practice is preferable to another.

Empathy

'A little fellow feeling in the bosom' (see jacket illustration of Mars, Venus and Cupid)

Extrovert

Define himself in terms of what is happening in the world about him. (Jung)

Factitious

(Not to be confused with fictitious, thought there are similarities). Illness that has been induced or invented, not naturally occurring. It may be unintentional, such as the untoward side effects of medication – iatrogenic – caused by doctors, or deliberate, such as Munchausen's Syndrome (see Chap. 2 – Diagnosis).

'False Memory Recall Syndrome'

May well be classified under brain washing. What happens is that a gullible girl falls under the influence of a charismatic convincing 'therapist' and is led to believe that her troubles are due to the 'fact' that she had been sexually abused, usually by her father, an accusation that is impossible to disprove. Then the Police are summoned, and 'evidence' taken. Many terrible injustices have occurred, innocent fathers accused and jailed, possibly committing suicide, and families broken up

Folie á deux
> A condition in which a delusion by one partner of a bonded pair is shared by the other one. The typical case is that of the criminal, in spite of all the evidence against him, is convinced of his innocence, and his wife is also similarly convinced. The saddest cases are those in which the husband becomes suicidal, and persuades his wife to join him in a suicide pact.

Fugue
> A flight from one's own identity. A behaviour disorder consequent upon intolerable anxiety and stress. See also 'Dissociation'.

Functional
> Commonly used to mean dysfunctional, to distinguish symptoms due to 'organic' or physical causes or pathology.

Gender (see below under 'Sex').

Hallucination
> A perception with no sensory stimulus. Visual hallucinations occur in toxic states and alcoholics, particularly in withdrawal situations – *delirium tremens*. Auditory hallucinations occur in schizophrenics. The 'voices' may be derogatory, accusatory, or instructive. At all events, they must be carefully assessed.

Homosexual (from Gk homo = same + sexual)
> The word is now considered inappropriate. It is acceptable to use the word 'gay' if two men are comfortable in bed with each other. 'Lesbian' refers to two women (see also intersex, Chapter 6). Bisexuals are comfortable with either or both (AC/DC)

Hypnagogic
> Hallucinatory experiences, auditory or visual, occurring during

dreaming. **Aristotle** regarded dreams as 'no more than the fragment-ed echo of the day's experiences.' **Sigmund Freud** thought they had special significance.

Hypnosis

A trance-like condition induced artificially, which results in a height-ened degree of suggestibility. A deep trance can be induced in 5% of people, but some resist it. The patient must be willing and co-operative. It is said that a post-hypnotic suggestion which would be morally or ethically forbidden, cannot be performed. The EEG of a patient in a trance is that of normal wakefulness. The German physi-cian **Anton Mesmer** (1734-1815) asserted that disease was due to obstruction of the free flow of nervous energy, which may be gravi-tational or magnetic, and he used magnets to 'cure' his patients. (This process appears in Mozart's comic opera 'Cosi fan Tutte'). He was a charismatic and powerful character and had a lucrative practice, which annoyed the traditional doctors. In 1784 the French King Louis XVI appointed a commission to investigate his claims. **Benjamin Franklin** and **Antoine Lavoisier** were appointed. They were unable to substantiate his claims and Mesmerism fell into dis-repute, as did Dr Mesmer.

A Manchester surgeon Dr **James Braid** (1795-1860) disputed Mesmer's claims and thought the wholeprocess could be explained by suggestion. In 1843 he wrote a book called *Neuropnology* and introduced the term 'hypnosis', and successfully treated cases of paralysis and aphonia. The technique essentially consists of causing an altered state of consciousness, a trance, in the patient by getting him or her to relax and respond to the therapists' suggestions, often by visual fixation, a candle or a swinging object. Belief plus expectation plus misdirected attention is the essence of the procedure.

But it is not without risk. A stage hypnotist regressed his 'victim' to the age of 10. Unfortunately at that age she had had a serious sex-ual assault by an 'uncle', which she had sensibly repressed in order to get on with her life (few girls have not had some unwelcome advances which most have sensibly ignored). But this one became seriously disturbed by the memory and suffered a nervous break-down. She sued the hypnotist and got £5000 damages.

Hypochondria

A condition, the various symptoms of which, were originally thought to be due to disorder of the spleen, which lies in the abdominal cavity on the left side under the ribs. This view is not longer held and nowadays 'hypochondriacs' are people obsessed with their 'health'

Hysteria

A behaviour disorder due to unresolved stress with manifestations which cannot be explained in terms of organic pathology. Sigmund Freud thought it could be classified into anxiety hysteria and conversion hysteria, in which all symptoms of anxiety have disappeared: 'La Belle Indifference'. It is said to be more common in the ill-educated but in Western society its full-blown manifestations are seldom seen now. There is usually a factor of secondary gain. Symptoms include hyperventilation, convulsions, blindness, amnesia (q.v.) paralyses, pains and anaesthesias. In the Middle Ages these were thought to be due to witchcraft and the victims were duly punished. In the First World War victims were called 'Shell Shocked'. Examination discloses no abnormality of the central nervous system, confirmed by PET brain scan.

Hysterical paralysis can also be diagnosed by a PET scan, where no expectation activity in the brain is found in response to a command. Treatment is said to be directed to the cause, and hypnosis has been popular but an intravenous infusion of a tranquiller may well be quicker (see Amnesia above – also Abreaction under Therapy). Mass hysteria occurs in certain emotionally stressful situations, erroneous ideas can 'infect' others by suggestion. In the past these bizarre manifestations were attributed to witchcraft and many unfortunate victims suffered. There is often a sexual background. A classical example is the trial of the Witches of Salem in 1692 when 19 women were hanged. Another is the mediaeval Dancing Mania (St Vitus' Dance) called now 'Collective Stress Reaction'. St Vitus' Dance is also a manifestation of Sydenham's Chorea, a complication of Rheumatic Fever, a condition seldom seen today. These symptoms would probably be classed as Post Traumatic Stress Disorder (see under Chapter 2 – Diagnosis). A curious example of hysterical behaviour is seen in pseudo-cyesis, in which the woman is convinced she is pregnant, but no baby is present. The abdomen distends, but nothing happens. There is a factor of secondary gain, to attract the attention of the husband. It happened to Mary Tudor, daughter of Henry VIII and wife of Phillip II of Spain(1554). It has even occurred in dogs.

Illusion

An inaccurate perception or interpretation of something actually and really perceived.

Insanity

This is as old as Mankind. It has three elements: 1. Thought disorder 2. Communication disorder. 3. Behaviour disorder. This latter causes problems with authority.

Instinct

The faculty of acting in such a way as to produce certain ends, without foresight of the ends, and without previous education or instruction in the performance

Intelligence

The ability to process information, similar to a calculator or computer. Many attempts have been made to measure it, with varying degrees of success, mainly to determine a person's fitness for a certain occupation or post. It is largely genetically determined (80% according to Sir **C. Burt**) as opposed to achievement, which depends mainly on environmental factors.

Internalisation (the inner voice)

The means by which language is processed into deeper layers of the mind, the intuitive, leading to thought and discursive analytic reasoning. Hence '*homo sapiens*'. Bilingual people sometimes revert to their primary language, the 'mother tongue' in times of emotional stress. In schizophrenia the barrier breaks down and the inner voice becomes 'outer' and the patient hears voices, auditory hallucinations. One must take great care to identify what the voices are saying to avert tragedy.

Introvert

Sees the world in terms of his own situation within it (Jung).

Masturbation

Mentioned with some trepidation. Some years ago in the USA a Surgeon-General expressed the view that it should be included in a syllabus of 'sex education.' He was forced to resign: an example of American prudishness, perhaps a relic of their Puritan ancestry. (In 2004 twenty television stations were fined $550,000 for inadvertently exposing the right breast of a female performer – Janet Jackson – for a brief period. Perhaps it would have been $1million if both breasts had been exposed).

The earliest mention of it is in the Bible, Genesis 18, v 9,&10. Onan, we are told, let his seed fall upon the ground, which displeased the Lord and He slew him. But Onan may just have been practising coitus interruptus. Masturbation is sometimes called onanism. This extraordinary story has been accepted by many Churches as justifying their belief that masturbation is 'a sin against the Holy Ghost' and therefore unforgivable, and thereby terrorising pubertal boys, and ensuring their destiny to hell.

What actually happens is that, at puberty, between the ages of 10–12, the anterior pituitary gland secretes growth and gonadotrophic hormones, causing enlargemant of the genitalia, and nocturnal erections and seminal emissions – wet dreams. These can be distressing and alarming as well as messy. In girls, menstrual periods start – the menarche. Neither of these can be considered sinful, merely physiological. Certain religious foundations used to get the boys up at 4.30am, to have a cold bath or shower, just as the hormone level is at its maximum. Heaven knows what damage this did to their fragile psyches. However, most of them survived and continued to grow. No doubt it was supposed to be character building. Some little girls get orgasms which may be mistaken for epileptic fits, and given inappropriate treatment.

> *My Brain it may rot*
> *Thank God I have not*
> *Got*
> *Disdiadochokinesis**

However, there is absolutely no evidence that masturbation causes either blindness or insanity

The extraordinary belief that masturbation causes insanity originated from the publication of a book called *Onania, or the Heinous Sin of Self-Pollution*, published anonymously but believed to be a clergyman turned quack, in about 1716. He produced pills at a guinea a box, guaranteed to cure it. (First one invents a disease, then a remedy for it. A recipe for riches. Times haven't changed).

A respectable Swiss physician, **Tissot**, published an account confirming this belief in 1758, and many peculiar procedures were tried to prevent it, with little success – bromide helped. It is an extraordi-

*the inability to perform repetitive movements.   15

nary evidence of the power of the printed word. Another is the publication of *Malleus Maleficarum (The Hammer of Witchcraft)* (1486) a book detailing the tests to determine witchcraft (it couldn't be proved, but on the other hand, it couldn't be disproved), which led to the deaths of thousands of innocent women. By the 20th century, with the decline of the notion of sin and the loss of the power of religion to influence people's thoughts and behaviour, this strange belief is no longer held.

One of the less edifying aspects of modern society is the extraordinary popularity of pornography, masturbation fantasy material, which has enabled many dubious and unsavoury characters to become extremely rich. The disgusting and appalling rise of paedophilia is another consequence of the desire for inappropriate gratification.

It is often said that masturbation is harmless provided not practised to excess. But what is excess? There was the case of the man who indulged for 2 hours, whereupon he developed a priapism, a persistent extremely painful erection of the penis, probably due to thrombosis of the penile veins. This is a medical emergency and in spite of treatment may well lead to permanent impotence.

Memory
This has three elements, reception, registration (retention) and recall, similar to a tape recorder. The microphone receives the information, the tape records it, playback recalls it. Memory in people is more complex, as emotion is involved. It can be divided into short term and long term memory, and the processes are very complex and poorly understood..

Munchausen Syndrome (see under Chapter 2 – Diagnosis).

Nervous Breakdown
A condition in which the patient is unable to function, due to non-physical or emotional causes. The portmanteau word 'Depression' is sometimes used.

Neurasthenia
A term no longer generally used, to describe general debility accompanied by symptoms of anxiety. Today it would probably be called 'depression', thanks to the introduction of the 'anti-depressants'.

A BRIEF HISTORY OF PSYCHIATRY

Neurosis/neurotic

A term introduced in 1772 by the Edinburgh physician Dr **William Cullen** to describe a condition in which the patient's symptoms could not be accounted for by physical or organic disease. The word 'functional' was added later but was abandoned in the 1930s. The word 'neurosis' was deleted from the 3rd edition of the *Diagnostic and Statistical Manual of Disease* (DSM III) in 1980.

Oedipus Complex

According to the legend as described in Homer's *Odyssey* (also in the play by Sophocles) Oedipus, King of Thebes, was destined to kill his father and marry his mother. When, on researching his ancestry, he learnt the truth, he put out his eyes, and his wife and mother, Jocasta, hanged herself. Perhaps the moral of the story is 'never look back'.

Sigmund Freud introduced the term and held that this 'complex' is the basis of some neuroses'. The Electra complex is the female equivalent. A girl wishes to kill her mother and marry her father.

Paranoia

Is a delusion held with great conviction, mainly at an emotional level, accompanied by feelings of persecution. Dr **Vladimir Bekhterev**, at the age of 70, was summoned to assess the mental condition of the Russian dictator Joseph Stalin. The good doctor described him as ill, even paranoid. How right he was. He died soon after, poisoned by Stalin (*Memoirs of Dmitry Shostakovich*). A similar fate befell Saddam Hussein's psychiatrist, who diagnosed paranoid schizophrenia, except that he was shot.

Personality Disorder (including borderline and multiple personality disorder)

The Classic Case is that of *The Strange Case of Dr Jekyll and Mr Hyde*, written by R.L. Stevenson in 1886. Though in this story the personality change is due to a chemical substance – in real life this is not necessary. It is probably due to a disturbed upbringing between the ages of 1 and 4, so that the child's sense of identity remains uncertain. Such people make good actors as they are able to take on another's identity effortlessly. But they do not make good husbands or wives.

The conflict in relationships unfortunately may lead to alcoholism or drug addiction (see under Chapter 2 – Diagnosis).

Placebo (Lat. = I will please)
A placebo is an intention or effect and operates equally powerfully whether the drug in question is pharmacologically active or inert, and depends on the confidence of the prescriber. A drug without pharmacological activity is a dummy.

Psychiatry
The branch of medicine which deals with the recognition, treatment and prevention of mental abnormalities and disorders. A psychiatrist is a qualified physician who has been trained and has experience in the diagnosis and treatment of psychiatric illness.

Psychosis
Loss of touch with reality (other people). Thought disorder, communication disorder, behaviour disorder.

Psychosomatic
Physical conditions such as asthma or eczema which are aggravated or accompanied by anxiety or stress, which can occur when the commitment exceeds the capability. There is often a genetic or hereditary element and some people have a lower anxiety threshold than others.

Psychedelic
A term introduced by the American psychiatrist **Humphry Osmond**. (1917-2004), in   association with the novelist **Aldous Huxley** in 1957, to describe the hallucinogenic effect of mescaline and LSD 25 (Lysergic acid diethylamide).
   Osmond used these drugs to some effect in the treatment of alcoholics. He was born and qualified in England. But he was involved with the CIA and MI6 as it was thought that these drugs could be used as 'truth drugs' when interrogating 'spies'. The use of these drugs fell into disrepute and they were declared illegal in 1970. He described a 'trip'as 'the most strange, most awesome, and among the most beautiful things in a varied and fortunate life'. The trouble is that some people can experience these semi-psychotic states years afterwards.

Psychopath
A person who appears to have little or no conscience, and will do the most appalling crimes with little feelings of guilt or remorse. It is thought to be genetic in origin and therefore 'untreatable'. However

there is some evidence from EEG studies that such persons suffer from delayed maturation of the necessary parts of the brain. Management involving punishment in seldom helpful.

Sometimes aggressive behaviour can be helped by proper nutrition (see also under Chapter 2 – Diagnosis – Personality Disorder)

Psychotherapy
The 'talking cure' – proposed and carried out by Dr Sigmund Freud and Dr Carl Jung, amongst others, at the end of the nineteenth century (see under Therapy – Chapter 3). Falling into disrepute as it tends to break up family relationships.

Sex
The word 'Sex' has changed its usage and meaning in the last few years. Historically and scientifically, it means the differentiation between male and female. Nowadays it is used as a pronoun and means sexual intercourse or copulation, or even sodomy (anal intercourse), or fellatio (oral intercourse), such as 'Did you have sex last night?' Even females can 'have sex' with each other (but who does what and with which and to whom?)

The word 'Gender' describes masculinity or femininity, the non-physical component of the personality. Also it has been used to differentiate proper nouns grammatically in Latin and the Latin languages such as Italian, French, Spanish. The English language does not recognize grammatical gender as it is felt to be pointless. Throughout this work, the words will be used in their original or historic meaning.

Synchronicity
Repeated experiences that indicated that events do not always obey the rules of time, space and causality (Jung). This may be an expression of the Buddhist belief – that personalities are transferable.

Therapy (see also Psychotherapy)
Many seek a living as a 'therapist', from acupuncture and aroma therapy through homeopathy to yoga and zen. Being essentially subjective they are not capable of objective or 'scientific' assessment as to their effectiveness, though many clients are helped and derive benefit.

Transference

The warm feeling of acceptance that the client feels in the presence of the therapist. Also counter-transference. The warm feeling of acceptance that the therapist feels in the presence of the client. This can lead to inappropriate sexual activity.

CHAPTER ONE

RELIGION, SCIENCE & MIND
(From *A Brief History of Science*)

Consciousness, being abstract, is hard to define. It is the basic non-phys-ical element. Evidence of it is shown in the response to stimuli, which may be either active or passive. It probably evolved, like everything else, as a response to the need of a primitive organism for food or a mate. At any rate, it appears to be the result of neuronal activity (there are estimated 10^9 neurones in a human brain). An essential feature of consciousness is mem-ory. This again is a consequence of neuronal activity, and may well be sim-ilar in nature to the memory of a calculator or computer. Synapses (the connections of nerve fibres in the brain) have features in common with the semiconductor junction, one of which is that they will allow the passage of an electric current one way but not the other.

There are several altered states of consciousness, with different causa-tion. The first two are physiological, the remainder, pathological.

1. Sleep. It is necessary to delete all the unwanted memories, particularly visual, that have accumulated during wakefulness, whether conscious or unconscious. The dolphin, an air breathing mammal, needs to surface from time to time. Apparently only half of its brain sleeps at a time. If it were not for this, it would drown.

2. Sexual arousal. This occurs during appropriate circumstances. It also occurs during paradoxical (REM – rapid eye movement) sleep.

3. Toxic delirium, such as high fever.

4. Hypnosis. This is a consequence of the learning process, or one might say, an exploitation of the learning process, used by demagogues. Religious and military exaltation may be a manifestation of mass hypnosis. Auto-hypnosis is also possible.

5. Drugs. Response to psychoactive drugs is unpredictable, may be lethal. Usually they make people happy but goofy. 'Trip' eloquently described by Henry James – 'a mood of vertiginous amazement at a meaningless infin-

ity'. Perhaps 'goofy' is better.

6. Epilepsy.

7. Hysteria (dissociation). Uncommon today in developed countries.

8. Head injury. Confusion leading to coma.

9. Brain disease, such as tumour or Alzheimer's disease.

Language is programmed into the infant by his or her mother. (This is similar to the 'booting' of a computer). It is stored in the brain – the passive mind (named thus by Aristotle – also called the *subconscious* by Sigmund Freud.) The computer analogue of the passive mind is the hard disk or memory chip. It is accessed by the active mind, the *conscious*. The conscious mind is the analogue of the central processing unit, with its random access memory. (Consciousness is the interface between the physical and the non-physical elements of the brain). Both the active and passive minds constitute the non-physical element of the personality. Just as some computers have more RAM than others, so some people's minds work faster than others. Consequent to this idea, the crashing of a computer has certain similarities to the nervous breakdown of *homo sapiens*. When a computer is presented with a task it cannot fulfil given its inadequate speed or memory or just that the task is impossible, it may crash, that is to say, it will not accept any input nor will it produce any output. The only thing to do is to switch it off and start again, or press the reset button if there is one. Likewise a person presented with an impossible situation, given his or her intellectual or emotional state, may cease to respond sensibly. The thing to do then is to switch off the brain by means of rest, TLC and appropriate medication until normal service is resumed. The French physician **Philippe Pinel** in 1792 released the shackles from the inmates of the Salpetrière in Paris, in the belief that there was nobody whose behaviour could not be improved by being treated with kindness rather than cruelty.

Learning appears to work mainly in a positive sense. One can persuade people to do things and believe things but it is difficult to persuade people not to do things. That is why anti-sex and anti-drug education and legislation are singularly unsuccessful.

In his long history of evolution, Man has developed language, in order to facilitate communication. Then came abstract thought, then came ideas, with the notion of God, then came writing. Then the *conscience* developed. This is epitomised in the *Golden Rule* – the perennial philosophy, common to all philosophies and religions – Do Unto Others as you Would that They Should do unto You. In the unfortunate condition of *psychopathy* sufferers appear not to have developed a conscience.

A *Totem* is an animal or the Spirit of an animal which gives the clan its name and with which it shares allegiance and mutual protection, and upon which the tribe may be dependent. The animal is respected, not always killed and eaten. In Hinduism, the spirits of the dead are believed to inhabit the bodies of monkeys, which are held sacred. Similar beliefs are found in Australian Aboriginal culture. Perhaps the totem of the early Judaeo/Christian religion was the sheep (*Agnus Dei*).

Animism is a primitive religion one feature of which is an altered state of consciousness induced by physical means, such as repeated mantras, drugs, whirling etc. It is the basis of *Astrology*. Early Man, gazing at the stars, identified patterns which were supposed to correspond to various animals. The character of the animal is in some way supposed to represent the character of the individual born under the particular constellation, and his or her future can be foretold by reference to his or her birth time and date. There has never been any evidence for the truth of this, yet many eminent individuals consult astrologers. Perhaps it is a way of transferring or avoiding responsibility for one's action.

Living creatures have 3 elements to be considered. Body (physical) – Mind (Non-physical) and Spirit. The Chinese have the word Qi or *Chi*, the Japanese the word *Reiki*, variously translated as 'life force' or nervous or emotional energy or even perhaps 'motivation'. There is no equivalent word in the English language, which makes discussion difficult. At any rate the principal underlying factor appears to be group activity. A group can accomplish more than the sum total of individual effort. Religion is a powerful motivating force. Love is a great stimulus to activity as, regrettably, is hate, especially jealousy.

Some people, the 'charismatic' have the ability to stimulate and control activity, the leaders of the world, for better or worse. They are at the top of the dominance hierarchy tree. Others have the ability to access people's passive memory or subconscious mind. They are the psychics or *mediums*, who sometimes claim to communicate with the dead – *necromancy*. Unfortunately this can lead to an emotional transference situation and dependency with loss of autonomy and money. Drugs, both legal and illegal, are increasingly used to stimulate nervous energy. Since the physiological balance is upset, increasing doses may be required to obtain the desired effect leading to dependency and addiction, with a corresponding loss of rational thought and social isolation, which is a significant factor in suicide.

The word "Religion" is derived from the Latin *religio* – 'I bind'. Therefore a religion is a group of people bound by a set of values or beliefs. 'A religion is not a pseudo-science invented to 'explain'. It is an intuitive response to a pitiless universe that historically gets hijacked by institutions'.

Man, by virtue of his nature as a social animal, tends to live in groups, and develop a dominance hierarchy system (similar to the 'peck order' of chickens) and from such groups leaders become identified, to whom the members defer, and owe loyalty and allegiance. The leader seeks to justify his position by asserting that his authority derives from God, Divine Right. Different ethnic groups have of course different names for this concept. The Ancient Egyptians had the Sun God Ra, (complete with halo), the Greeks had Zeus, The Romans, Jupiter, the Hebrews Jehovah, the Muslims Allah, and so on. There was always a close relation between the leader (King) and his High Priest (Shaman, who had direct communication with God). The King chose the High Priest, and the Priest crowns the King, thereby giving him legitimacy. It became necessary to separate the various administrative functions, and specialisation occurred, and gods of war, fertility, agriculture, love, wine etc., were postulated, together with their priests and priestesses, all of whom enjoyed prestige and privilege. Today we have various Governmental Ministries and Departments.

In the Hindu dominance hierarchy or *caste* system as it known, the Priest or Brahmin is the highest, then comes the soldier, then the farmer, then the clerk, then the cleaner (untouchable). Justification for this established order of things and social position calls for faith – belief – not evidence. The origin of these systems of belief is not clear. They may well have evolved in order to justify territorial expansion 'God is on our side' – 'It is God's will', or merely to justify the status quo. The notion of survival after death is clearly of advantage to the military, fear of death and its avoidance is the fundamental fear of all living creatures.

Since Religion is based on Faith, and Science is based on Reason and evidence, there is inevitably a logical and intellectual conflict. In fact the two are irreconcilable. It may well be that the two are necessary for emotional and rational development and evolution. One can no more deny the world of emotion or feeling or instinct than one can deny the world of reason. The two are complementary and necessary.

A *Theocracy* can be considered as a combination of State and Religious power whose function is to keep the community together, to prevent its destruction by perceived outside interference, just as an organism seeks to preserve its identity and autonomy by developing immune reactions against microbes. This is the basis of *paranoia*, when perceived dangers become irrational and mental balance is disturbed. Sometimes the physiological immune response itself becomes destructive, when the body starts manufacturing antibodies against itself, with the development of auto-immune diseases.

Perhaps the last theocracy is the Buddhist Tibet, with its God/King, the Dalai Lama. It struggles to survive as an independent entity, in the face of relentless progress, as its principle of non-violence renders it vulnerable to external force.

Many people find scientific determinism unacceptable. People like to think that they do have some higher purpose in life, that their activities and thoughts do have consequences, that there is more to life than mere survival and reproduction, that all is not predetermined.

Then there is the concept of *free will*. This is best explained by analogy. A billiard ball does not have free will. Its movements are entirely a consequence of past events. A sentient being, on the other hand has alternatives – he can go to the right or the left depending not only on past events but on future desires, intentions or consequences. An inanimate object has no such choice. If one defines intelligence as the ability to process information, a beetle is as intelligent as a computer, except that a beetle, unlike a computer, has free will in that he can go to the right or the left in pursuit of that which will confer advantage to it.

Consider the question 'why is the Earth round?'

A Theology student might answer 'God made the Earth round so that we should not see too far what lay ahead'.

A Science student might answer 'The spherical configuration of the globe exists on account of the operation of the second law of thermodynamics, in that this shape maximizes its entropy.

Both answers might be considered correct, though quite incomprehensible to the opposite discipline.

Science deals with the objective, Religion with the subjective. Both are necessary, and complementary.

The French philosopher and mathematician **Rene Descartes** (1596-1650) is known for his saying 'cogito ergo sum' – I think therefore I am. It might well be more appropriate to say 'Credo ergo sum' – I believe therefore I am. Integrity of the personality depends on a system of belief. One can consider the brain as a computer which is programmed from birth, firstly with language then with belief, though the two are inextricably interwoven. 'Give me a child until he is seven and he is mine for life' claims the Jesuit. It is no coincidence that the brain continues to grow until the age of seven. A brain injured child under the age of seven can grow up with no detectable deficit. After that age there may well be some impairment.

In order to understand the nature of belief one can start by considering the placebo effect. A *Placebo (*Latin – I will please) is an effect or intention rather than a tablet or medication. It operates equally whether the medication is pharmacologically active or pharmacologically inactive, and depends on the attitude of the practitioner. It is particularly effective in non-physical conditions such as headaches, to the extent that 30% of people will experience relief from a 'dummy' tablet devoid of pharmacological activity. Some people respond better then others – they could be called 'placebo responders' or perhaps 'suggestible'. The more powerful the suggestion, the more effective the response. Witch doctors, ngangas, are expert at this and can even persuade people to death. Likewise, they can also be credited with magical cures. Objective belief requires evidence. Subjective belief does not – merely powerful suggestion. Those who seek evidence for the existence of God are doomed to disappointment, since the notion of God is abstract, not objective but subjective, no less real for some, or necessary.

Many of the most sublime manifestations of music, art and architecture have been based on Religious dedication – To the Glory of God, even though the composers, artists, architects and masons concerned may not have been particularly pious. It is interesting to speculate that Stone Circles, the most splendid of which is Stonehenge, perhaps represents Man's early need to delineate a piece of territory, which, having been consecrated, is devoted to the performance of symbolic rituals associated with the chiefs and dominant families of the tribe, who claim leadership and possession of the territory. Also with the performance of rituals associated with those three elements of family life – birth, marriage and death; significant events in effecting the cohesion of the family and loyalty of the tribe. Perhaps Westminster Abbey would be the modern equivalent. Westminster Abbey is but 1000 years old, whereas Stonehenge is 3,800 years old.

And yet it is hard to believe that evolution has occurred purely as a result of random activity, that all that has been or will be is purely chance. Statistically, it seems unlikely; and that there is an underlying purpose driving it all, whatever that may be. 'Once', said Winston Churchill, after a particularly good dinner, 'I thought I understood the meaning and purpose of life. Unfortunately, by the following morning, I had forgotten what it was.'

Religion, like everything else, has evolved as a response to need. Behavioural change, from primitive to more complex and elaborate practices and beliefs, is based on the obligatory Primate instincts, the necessity to Belong, to Create, to Communicate and to Explore. Particularly, to answer questions such as 'where have we come from?' and 'where are we going?' And Religion provides an answer to the questions that Science cannot. Fear of death and its aftermath is fundamental. 'Losing God changed my whole outlook – it left Fear as the dominant emotion'.(Wendy Perriam). Therefore Religion is about Belonging and about Death. There is nothing like a funeral to remind people of God. 'Ashes to Ashes, Dust to Dust' as the mortal (physical) remains are committed to Earth or Fire or Water. But the Soul (non-physical) goes Marching On.

We, like all living creatures, have been allotted by Divine Providence, or perhaps Inscrutable Fate, depending on one's belief, a certain amount of time and a certain amount of space. We must use it creatively (good) rather then destructively (bad).

A sensible philosophy of life is to look forward, not backward. What is done is done and cannot be undone.

CHAPTER TWO

ORIGINS

Evolutionary change is brought about by two factors, one external, that is to say, climate, food supply, and predators; the other internal, genetic roulette, the effect of mutation on the structure and functioning of the individual.

Current belief in the Origin of Mankind suggests that we share a common ancestor with ape-like animals who lived over 100,000 years ago (perhaps 1 million) in the African forests and plains. (Our nearest relative, the chimpanzee, contains 99% of our DNA). It is tempting to suggest that a cataclysmic climate change occurred in which the plains became flooded, forcing our ancestors to take to the waters and become essentially aquatic. This would explain our loss of hair, except in the axillary, and pubic regions and on the head, and the accumulation of subcutaneous fat – unique amongst Primates. (The Cave of Swimmers as depicted in the film 'The English Patient' suggests this. In addition, teenage girls are often excellent swimmers, perhaps presenting a stage in evolution. Perhaps the desire of some pregnant women to give birth under water – birthing baths – is another indication. Also mammals such as whales and dolphins give birth under water. Similarly, pre-pubertal boys make tree houses, representing an earlier, arboreal stage. This is the Recapitulation Theory). At the same time, the diet changed and fish were added to the diet of fruit and meat and cereals. Fish contain significant amounts of the essential fatty acids linolenic and linoleic acids, which are converted in the body to DHA and EPA, necessary for the formation of phospho-lipids, essential for cell membrane structure. (see Appendix 1). An essential fatty acid is one that cannot be synthesised in the body. These chemicals are needed in the formation of nervous tissue and it is possible that this was the stimulus to the rapid development of the brain. The assumption of the upright position could also follow from the emergence from the waters. All this is of course pure speculation.

The discovery of fire was attributed by the early Greeks to Prometheus, who stole it from the Gods. As a punishment he was chained to a rock and by day ravens pecked out his liver. By night, his liver grew again. Even then our ancestors were aware of the amazing regenerative powers of the liver. Be that as it may, men became aware that cooked meat was more palatable and more easily digested than raw meat and hence a better 'protein harvest' enabling people to survive in hard times. Meat could be preserved by drying and by salting. It is possible that cooking occurred in those regions where methane gas issues from the soil or rocks, which results in a perpetual fire. Such areas are to be found in Armenia and probably ancient Greece.

With development of the brain came the notion of self-consciousness and conscience. Children under the age of 5 are remarkably un-selfconscious and are quite happy running around in the nude, just as primitive tribes are. Then came the desire to cover the genitals and the feeling of shame should they not be covered. This is the symbolised by the Fall of Man – expulsion of Adam and Eve from the Garden of Eden and depicted in **Burghers**' painting (frontispicce). (Genesis 3 v7 – 'They Knew that they were Naked'. They became aware of the Knowledge of Good and Evil, as it was from this tree that they had picked the forbidden fruit – choice.). This was the beginning of the sense of conscience and morality, encapsulated in the phrase – 'Do unto Others as you would that They should do unto You' – the Golden Rule.

Mankind became aware of the reality of death and the necessity of performing suitable ceremonies. Re-cycling of dead animals in nature is performed at night by the scavengers, hyenas jackals and wolves, and by day, Vultures and Marabou Storks. In order to avoid this ignominious fate, burial or cremation was performed, supervised by an elder of the tribe, the Priest, who had special powers. These ceremonies reached their zenith about 5000 BC, in Egypt, with the Pharoahs. Elaborate rituals including mummification were instituted and the construction of the giant Pyramids ensured the safe passage of the Pharoah into the 'afterworld'.

Sounds became words, with emotional as well as intellectual content:

'Words are to us, the medium of thought; we cannot conceive of things except by their names. We cannot muse, contrive, imagine, resolve or reject, nay we cannot love or hate but in acting upon those passions in the very form of words. If we dream 'tis in words, we speak everything to ourselves; and we know not how to think, or act, or intend to act, but in the form of words; all our passions and affections are acted in words and we have us no other way for it.' (Daniel Defoe – 1796)

Possibly the earliest form of writing- the record of the spoken word, linear B or perhaps Sanscrit. The hieroglyphics of the Egyptian Pharoahs (5,000 BC) gave way to Greek, with its distinctive alphabet of 26 characters. In the Middle East, our earliest history was the Old Testament, written in Hebrew, a language similar to Arabic. Morality needed to be codified and written down. Hence Exodus Chapter 20 v 3-17 – The Ten Commandments.

Historically, management of insanity (disturbance of thought, communication and behaviour) has gone through various phases, depending on the perception of the cause and nature of the condition. During the Middle Ages the cause was thought to be demoniacial possession, a religious condition. A priest was summoned, for purposes of exorcism.(Suggestion is very powerful). If this failed, restraint, torture and punishment were used, and the afflicted were cast into dungeons. But a large number were imprisoned and it became apparent that there was a distinction between the mad and the bad (see Chapter 7). Unfortunately this distinction is not always maintained even today.

In 1247 the Bethlehem Royal Hospital was founded by **Simon Fitzmary** originally at Bishopsgate, London, as the Priory of the Brethren and Sisters of the Order of the Star of Bethlehem . The name became corrupted to 'Bedlam' later in the 18th century, owing to the chaos and disorder therein. It became infamous for the cruel and brutal treatment of its inmates.

New Bethlem Hospital, 1676

In 1676 it was rebuilt, the New Bethlem, 'The most Magnificent Hospital Building in Europe', designed by **Robert Hooke**, more like a palace than a hospital, with the much respected Dr **Edward Tyson** M.D., F.R.S. as it's Physician. He was a man of science, not given to idle speculation, the founder of comparative anatomy, the first to describe the anatomy of the chimpanzee.

He was a practising physician, with a large practice. He realised that physical well-being was as important as mental, and ensured that the patients were cleaned, properly clothed, fed and cared for. In 1693 a female nurse was employed, and in 1700 an out-patient department established. In spite of the treatment meted out, consisting of blood-letting, purging and emetics, Tyson reckoned that two thirds of his patients recovered, and there was a long waiting list for admission. Between 1684 and 1703 out of 1,294 patients in the hospital, 890 were cured and discharged

His death in 1708 marked the end of an era, and a period of stagnation set in which was to last 100 years. Until 1795, when the apothecary **John Haslam** was appointed, the hospital languished in a sterile conservatism. Many notable artistic and literary people visited the hospital , including Hogarth, Samuel Johnson, Nathaniel Lee and Christopher Smart, the latter two were patients at one time. In 1733 Hogarth painted a series of pictures

Hogarth's 'The Rakes Progress'. In the background the Rake's wife is being comforted.

from life, 'The Rakes Progress' faithfully portraying the incurable ward, with its cells and staircase.

Dean Swift was elected a Governor in 1717 and in 1745 founded an asylum in Dublin, the first hospital for the charitable care of the insane in Ireland.

Bethlem was the only public institution in the whole kingdom caring for lunatics in the 18th century, though there were numerous private asylums, to which troublesome wives or daughters could be committed. Abuse was rife. In 1773 a Bill was passed by the Commons to control these – 'The Regulation of Private Madhouses,' but was thrown out by the Lords.

In the 17th and 18th centuries it became a place of entertainment and fees were charged for gawking at the antics of the inmates, a disgraceful practice that was ended in 1770. By 1800 the palatial building was no more than 'an elegant hulk'.and in 1801 the Third Bethlem Hospital was opened at St. George's Field in 1815, with 120 beds. 'Treatment' consisted of bleeding, vomiting and purging. The Hospital was relocated to Beckenham, Kent in 1930.

In 1771 St. Luke's Hospital was opened in Moorfields, paid for by City Gentlemen and public subscription. Dr **William Battie** was appointed physician and in its first 10 years 749 patients had been received, 363 discharged cured, 198 remained uncured, 39 died. In these early days handcuffs and leg locks were still in use. William Battie was a renowned physician and was the first to lecture on mental diseases and to allow medical students into the hospital. His book was the first English medical textbook to devote itself solely to psychiatric disorders. He warned against the practices of purging and blood-letting and stressed that even severe mental illness could recover in time with good nursing.

In Newcastle upon Tyne a Hospital was opened in 1764

On May 10th, 1766 a hospital was opened in Manchester for 'Poor Lunaticks', to add to the Dispensary and Infirmary, with the following rules:

Every patient, on admission, was to be carefully examined, and if there were any wounds, sores, or bruises, The Physician or Surgeon was to be informed of them.

No stripes or beatings, then so freely used by Keepers, no coercion whatever more than was necessary, to restrain the Furious from hurting themselves or others, were to be inflicted , or made use of by the Keeper, or any of his Servants: and no medicines were to be forcibly administered unless by special Order in Writing from the Physician, upon pain of expulsion. The feet of those in straw, or chains, were to be carefully examined , gently rubbed, night and morning, and covered with flannel during the winter season, and notice given to the Physician or Surgeon should any injury have taken place.

The Male and Female patients were kept separate, upon different stories of the Hospital; and commodious apartments were appointed for the convalescents so that they were not disturbed by noisy or violent patients.

All were aired in different yards appointed for the purpose as often as possible.

As the Hospital was designed, in great part, to help persons who could afford to pay for their maintenance and treatment, separate accommodation was provided from that for the paupers was provided for them; and after a few years the part of the hospital which the better class occupied was called the Asylum.

The House Visitors of the Infirmary visited the Hospital and Asylum daily to observe the behaviour of the Keeper, Matron, and servants toward the patients, and in particular to examine the bedding and nightly accommodation of each patient, for which purpose they occasionally visited in the evening:

There is to be no sightseeing by the curious as in London Public Hospitals. No relation or friend of a patient was allowed admittance without an order in writing from one of the managers for the time being, or one of the Physicians or Surgeons or Weekly Board: and no stranger was admitted but on the same terms, all which orders had to be filed and kept by the Governor for the inspection of the Trustees.

The Physicians were to visit their patients at least twice weekly and oftener when necessary. The House Apothecary (the Resident Medical Officer) of the infirmary was to inspect the whole Hospital and Asylum every day.

Consultations were to be held monthly or more Frequently by the Physicians concerning the cases of the patients by which experience and knowledge could be reciprocally be communicated in a disease of all others the most perplexing and obscure. Regular journals and records were to be kept. No patient was to be discharged without consultation of the physicians.

These regulations, when implemented, prevented many of the grosser abuses that occurred in many other institutions, and Manchester was exonerated from criticism. .

In its first year, the hospital treated 36 patients. 13 were discharged as cured, 2 as much relieved.

In 1773 the hospital was enlarged to 42 wards and in 1787 enlarged to 80 beds and 120 patients were treated. At this time it was still the only public institution of its kind in the North West of England, far too small to accommodate all those who sought admission.

In 1798 Sir **Alexander Crichton** (1763-1856) wrote a treatise 'An Inquiry into the Nature and Origin of Mental Derangement,' largely based on German work, and describing symptoms and signs to form various diagnostic categories, using **Linnaeus**' classification into Genera and Species, Orders and Classes. (Linnaeus had published 'Systema Naturae' in 1735)

Crichton was an Edinburgh graduate, served his apprenticeship under **Alexander Wood**, the Surgeon, and took his M.D. in Leyden in 1735. He studied at Paris, Stuttgart, Vienna and Halle, but, disliking surgery, returned to London and was elected Physician to the Westminster Hospital in 1795. In 1804 he was appointed Physician in Ordinary to the Russian Czar, Alexander I. Within a few years he became head of the civil medical department, and was befriended by the dowager Empress. On his return to England, he was Knighted by George IV at Brighton Pavilion in 1821.

In 1792, in the wake of the French Revolution, Philippe Pinel struck the chains from the inmates of the Bicêtre and Salpetrière Hospitals in Paris, and 'called upon the world to realize the horrible injustice done to this wretched and suffering class of humanity'. First to be set free was an Englishman. He had been in chains for 40 years, no one knew his history except that he had killed one of his Keepers with a blow from his manacle.

Manchester Hospital, 1773

He was greatly feared. Pinel entered his cell and said 'Captain, I will order your chains to be taken off and to give you liberty to walk in the Court, if you will promise me to behave well and injure no-one.' The chains were removed and the captain staggered to the door of his cell – his first look was to the sky, and he said 'how beautiful!'. For the next two years he remained in the Bicêtre, helping other patients, with no return of his paroxysms. Pinel unshackled 53 patients, and the success of his experiment was assured.

In 1801 Pinel wrote a book, *Traité de la Manie*, which was an academic study of mental disorders.

In Germany in 1811 I.**C.A Heinroth** was appointed to to the first chair of .mental therapy in Leipzig.

In 1828 this was renamed the chair of Psychiatry, and the specialty flourished in France and Germany.

In 1865 **William Griesinger** was appointed first Professor of Psychiatry and Neurology in Berlin. Other Chairs were established in Bonn, Heidelberg, Gottingen, Zurich and Vienna. The relationship between psychiatric disorders and brain pathology was investigated.

A BRIEF HISTORY OF PSYCHIATRY

In 1879 **Wilhelm Wundt** (1832-1920) started the world's first psycho-logical laboratory at the University of Leipzig. Two years earlier, two Cambridge physiologists **James Ward** and **John Venn**, tried to open one in Cambridge. They were refused on the grounds that 'a theologically minded mathematician would insult religion by putting the human soul on a pair of scales'. In 1888, a pupil of Wundt, the American **James Cattell**, became the world's first Professor of Psychology in Philadelphia.

Throughout the 19th century there was remarkably little enthusiasm for the establishment of academic centres for research into neuro-psychiatric disease, except in Germany.

In France **Jean-Marie Charcot** (1825-1893) treated patients with hys-terical symptoms with hypnosis. He was a great showman and created the greatest neurological clinic of the day at the Salpetrière Hospital. He set about classification of the nervous diseases. He described the three classi-cal signs of multiple (disseminated) sclerosis- scanning speech, intention tremor and nystagmus (Charcot's Triad). He described the lightning pains of tabes dorsalis (a manifestation of tertiary syphilis) and in 1886 the famil-ial peroneal muscular atrophy of Charcot-Marie-Tooth disease. From 1872-1887 he recorded his observations in his book *Leçons sur les mal-adies du système nerveux faites à la Salpètriere*. But his use of hypnosis came increasingly into question.

Throughout the 18th century the mentally afflicted were still treated bru-tally throughout Europe largely because it was cheaper. In more civilised communities attendants had to be paid. With the collapse of the religious dogma that illness was due to sin and was God's punishment, things grad-ually improved. In France, in 1838, they were accommodated in hospitals specially designed for the purpose. In England during the Victorian age, many asylums were likewise constructed. Masters in Lunacy, lawyers, were appointed to supervise these, as lunacy was considered a legal rather than a medical condition.

In 1791 a Quaker girl died in suspicious circumstances in York Asylum and in 1796 the Retreat was founded in York, by **William Tuke**, a Quaker, managed by openness and kindness and was described as the best regulat-ed establishment in Europe. Warm baths were used to control the manic, and sleep was induced by a full meal.

In 1808 the *County Asylums Act* established Institutions for the care of the indigent. These were to be funded by fees or the parish. They were to be supervised by the local magistrates.

In 1845 the *Lunacy Act* established the creation of institutions to be funded by general taxation. It was believed that recovery was impossible, and it was this that led to appalling overcrowding as no one could be discharged. A doctor could be employed if there were more than 100 patients.

Middlesex County Lunatic Asylum was established in 1861, the year of the Great Exhibition, at Colney Hatch, Friern Barnet, North London, for 'paupers' that is to say those whose relatives could not afford the fees of better places, the Private Sector such as Crichton Royal in Edinburgh or St. Andrew's Northampton. Colney Hatch was originally designed for 1000 patients, but, such was the demand that in 1853 268 patients were turned away. In 1869 there were 2,261 patients and it had expanded to 2,700 in 1927 an all time high. It was surrounded by a 10 foot wall, though whether this was designed to keep patients in or to keep them out was not clear.

In the USA there were hospitals for up to 5,000 patients. Wards would have up to 100 patients. There were few doctors, the staff were largely untrained, and the hospitals were largely run by the patients. (This regrettable situation sometimes occurs in jails.).

Colney Hatch had a chapel, a cemetery, workshops, productive vegetable gardens and was a community under the direction of the Medical Superintendant. There was an assembly hall in which concerts, lectures and exhibitions were held. Admission was a legal process, directed by a magistrate, with certification. Doctors were employed largely to attend to the physical ailments of the inmates, of which tuberculosis and dysentery, erysipelas and syphilis (GPI- general paralysis of the insane) were common. They had no knowledge of the mental history of their patients so psychotherapy was low on the list of treatments.

In 1905 Dr **A.P. von Wassermann** – (German bacteriologist 1866-1925) discovered the complement fixation test for syphilis. This was a real advance as it gave a physical or organic cause for the patients' illness and symptoms, – tertiary syphilis – occurring many years after the original infection. Some institutions had between 20-40% of male admissions with GPI. (AIDS, the Acquired Immunodeficiency Syndrome has a similarly delayed clinical picture). The causative organism, a spirochaete, *Treponema Pallidum*, could be inhibited by mercury containing compounds. (A night with Venus leads to a lifetime with Mercury). But mercury is a metal and heavy metals are extremely toxic to biological systems and many patients died of mercury poisoning (tremor – hatters' shakes – mercury was used in the manufacture of hats – and psychosis) – rather than syphilis.

It had been observed that treponema pallidum lost its activity when heated and in 1917 Professor **Julius Wagner-Jauregg** at the University of Vienna found that, by causing a high fever by infecting the patient with malaria, neuro-syphilis could be arrested. (Similarly, remission has sometimes been observed in schizophrenics during a febrile illness such as 'flu, only to relapse when the fever abates. For a possible explanation see Appendix 1) The malaria was then treated with quinine. This was the first virtual cure of a major mental illness and the Professor won the Nobel Prize in 1927. Nowadays penicillin would be used, as the organism is sensitive to it. But the problems associated with neurosyphilis have in recent times been replaced by similar 'brain failure' associated with AIDS.

Patients were sedated using chloral hydrate, bromide and later, barbiturates. Perhaps the greatest advance in the treatment of behaviour disorder was the discovery and introduction of the drug Largactil (chlorpromazine – a derivative of histamine) in the 1950s which achieved sedation without inhibiting respiration and led the way to closure of many of the large institutions.

— • —

Whilst in Germany there were several research institutions devoted to 'nervous diseases' and the diagnosis and treatment of insanity at the end of the 19th century and the beginning of the 20th, in England there were none. This was remedied in 1946, when Sir **Aubrey Lewis** (1900-1975) was elected Professor of Psychiatry of the University of London, in succession to Prof. **E. Mapother**, who was the first professor. The Bethlem Royal and the new Maudsley were united to create the Institute of Psychiatry, making a 500 bed teaching centre.

Sir **Henry Maudsley** (1835-1918) as a student at University College London, won 10 gold medals. After experience in asylums he decided to specialise in psychiatry. He married the daughter of Dr John Connelly a psychiatrist. He served as medical superintendent of the Manchester asylum and was subsequently appointed Professor of Medical Jurisprudence at

University College. He wrote a textbook on mental illness *Physiology and Pathology of the Mind* in 1867' .

He had a large and lucrative practice and gave the London Council a large sum of money with which to found the research institute and teaching centre associated with his name. He had modelled his original Hospital on **Emil Kraepelin**'s Department of Psychiatry in Munich, and dealt with neuro-science and clinical psychiatry. It was the first, and for long, the only teaching and research unit in England and was a powerful influence in upgrading the training and practice of psychiatry in Britain. There was a 3 year course for trainee psychiatrists, with regular seminars and case conferences. The Maudsley Hospital had been opened in 1923 as an acute psychiatric Hospital, paid for by the London County Council and the University of London. Lewis was the outstanding British research psychiatrist of the 20th Century. .

The ideal concept is that there should be small hospitals for the acutely disturbed which should be established for all cities of about 50,000 people, and of colonies for chronic patients to be established in rural districts adjacent to the cities – a refuge ' from the slings and arrows of outrageous fortune.'

In 1952 the wards were unlocked. In the 1960's the view was held that many of the 'long-stay' patients were suffering 'institutional neurosis', due to their long incarceration, and abandonment by families, if any, and discharge was not feasible. But with the introduction of the phenothiazines in 1956 demand fell and many of the asylums were demolished and the inmates released into 'care in the community', with uncertain results as provision for their care had not been properly considered nor properly instituted.

In the UK Mental Health Acts classify patients as 'voluntary' or 'involuntary' for their admission into a Psychiatric Hospital. Compulsory admission involves a Social Worker and an appointed Doctor to sign a 'Section' under the Mental Health Act, which may be for 3 or 28 days, after which the case is reviewed. The application for admission is addressed to the Medical Director of the appropriate hospital.

The management of the depressed, unhappy and disturbed has gone through many phases, depending on the perceived nature and cause of the condition. Most of such 'patients' are cared for and treated by relatives, families and the ubiquitous GP, and medication if thought necessary. In the developing world the local 'healers' or witch doctors perform this function, but frequently their advice is so bizarre that the situation may be made worse.

In the UK the Priory Hospitals Group has 15 hospitals or clinics managed on a private fee-paying basis though about 60% of its beds are paid for via NHS Trusts, for those considered suitable for in-patient treatment. The fees can amount to £1000 to £3000 per week. For a proper alcoholic detoxication programme including group therapy and possibly cognitive behaviour therapy lasting 6-12 weeks, this can cost as much as heart-bypass surgery. Claims of 70% 'cure' = non-relapse after 1 year, are made. NHS clinics with a reduction and replacement regime are not as effective.

Status
One of the biological characteristics of social animals is to develop a status heirarchy, with dominant animals controlling subordinate ones. One can observe this in the young of various species, where 'play' is in fact a means of establishing this. Biologically it means the survival of the fittest. This is particularly noticeable in chickens, where the weakest hen gets pecked to death. In pigs, the runt of the litter develops a craftiness in order to survive, being quicker to notice an available nipple when his big brothers and sisters fall off, satisfied. The dominant individual (alpha) is the most powerful, able to control the tribe and to defeat 'enemies' thus ensuring the survival of the tribe and the individuals in it. In modern times these are the 'war lords'. With the invention of guns and explosives this system has become totally disordered, and many of the casualties of war are not the combatants but women and children and other non-combatants. This is particularly found in the so-called 'developing' world. The subordinate individuals might be designated 'gamma', with a whole range in between. Most of the patients of the psychiatrists come from the gammas. Status is also derived from parentage. If one's father is a king one is automatically a prince or princess, whether one likes it or not. In this context, status is indicated in terms of altitude, 'Your Highness'.

Considerations of status must be investigated in cases of bullying, either by siblings, classmates or even parents, in which 'blame' is always shifted onto the subordinate individual. This, naturally leads to much unhappiness and may even lead to suicide. Ideally, the tormentor and the tormented must be allowed to express their grievances and experiences, in front of a neutral adjudicator (not authority – as that would lead to accusations of 'sneaking', with unhelpful consequences), and a friend, witness to fact – noting that bullies are often liars as well as cowards. But they can make people very unhappy. They often rise to high office in politics, the military, the professions and commerce.

Status in family relationships can be a source of much misery, and sometimes even death. Children who are somewhat different from the accepted 'norm' are used as scapegoats, accused as being 'evil' and blamed for all family misfortunes. In primitive cultures exorcism is used to 'expel the evil spirits', and sometimes the unfortunate child dies.

Evidence of status is found in headgear. At the top of course, is the Crown. In Victorian and Edwardian times the top hat was higher than the bowler, which was higher than the flat cap. Now that few people wear hats this form of class distinction has lapsed except hunters and undertakers. Primitive tribes sometimes have elaborate headgear to denote status.

The ancient custom of *droit de seigneur* lampooned in Mozart's comic opera 'the Marriage of Figaro' was a means by which the head of the tribe or high priest had the right of first sexual intercourse with the bride. One of the troubles of this was that half-brothers became insanely jealous of each other, often resorting to murder. The strongest genes were therefore present in the offspring, who, in addition, had instinctive loyalty to the tribe. Also, since first intercourse can be a painful and embarrassing experience for the female, at least this was minimised by having someone experienced who knew what was required. In recent times it is not considered fair so it has been abandoned. It still remains true that girls 'throw themselves' at the rich and powerful and famous, perhaps a throw back to earlier times. Power is a great aphrodisiac.

The Hindu caste system has existed for over 2000 years. The word comes from the 16th Century Portuguese travellers who applied their word for 'clan' – *casta* – to describe the segregated groups they observed in Indian society. This ideal society was established at the time of Creation, according to the Brahmins, the Hindu Priests. Society was divided into four separate classes. At the top, were the Brahmins. Next came Kings and Warriors (*kshatriya*) followed by Farmers and Merchants, (*vaishyas*), last of all, the serfs (*shudras*). They were forbidden to learn of the sacred scriptures (*vedas*). From laundrymen to potters, moneylenders, gardeners,oil-pressers, even thieves and whores, all knew their place in society according to their trade. Castes are ranked according to their purity, with the 'dalis', untouchables, at the bottom of the heap. Even the sight of the lowest 'once born' would contaminate the 'twice born' Brahmin. Although legislation has been passed to abolish the system, many aspects of caste still govern life in modern India. Given this system, it is understandable that intermarriage is frowned upon, to the extent that girls who marry or attempt to marry outside their caste may be put to death. A similar arrangement exists in the more primitive regions of Islam.

In the great game of snakes and ladders that is life, there is no problem if one lands on a ladder. But landing on a snake is a different matter. Loss of self-esteem and status leads to 'depression', and the person may seek psychiatric help. Never give up! Who knows, your next throw might land you on a ladder!

The status of psychiatric patients tends to be low. This is sometimes called 'stigma'. The status of a physician tends to reflect that of the status of his or her patients. Thus the physician to the King might be considered a doctor of high status, with a corresponding long list of patients waiting to consult him, with corresponding high fees. The structure of the NHS should, by virtue of being a salaried rather than a fee paying service, help to eliminate this class distinction. Since it is jealousy rather than love that makes the world go round, it is jealousy that makes high status people such as kings, presidents and celebrities the victims of attack by low status people.

The late Professor **Liam Hudson** said 'the high status psychologist works in a laboratory, with rats. The low status psychologist works with human beings, in their natural habitat.' It is tempting to suggest that it is the latter whose contribution is the greater.

Confidentiality
One of the major problems of psychotherapy is the matter of secrecy, usually called confidentiality. A classic example of 'family therapy' happens when a young girl, said to be 'disturbed' is actually the victim of sexual or physical abuse by a parent, often a step-father in present times, with the increasing break up of families. The parent of course denies this and the girl becomes a scapegoat, is disbelieved, becomes anorexic, sometimes suicidal. Sometimes the mother condones the situation, so as to avoid blame falling on herself. The therapist has to try to untangle the family relationships, which can be difficult in a situation in which secrecy is para-

mount. On the other hand the 'recovered memory' syndrome must always be borne in mind, to exclude allegations of impropriety which may have been implanted by the therapist.

The Hippocratic oath had something to say about secrecy. Unfortunately, with increasing 'right to know' legislation, this is becoming very difficult.

Responsibility
One of the principal functions of a doctor is to accept responsibility for the patient, and hence blame when something goes wrong. In a litigious society this can be avoided somewhat by referring patients to someone else, thus building up long 'waiting lists'. This is a particularly onerous burden for the psychiatrist, whose patients may go on to kill themselves or even worse, someone else. To be on the safe side admission for observation may be done. It takes courage for the psychiatrist and the social worker to decide to admit a patient to hospital compulsorily. It takes courage on occasions not to. Whatever the decision, it is essential for the protection and integrity of all concerned – patient, relatives, psychiatrist, social worker, GP – that there should be an effective and independent court of appeal to which any of them can apply, for an honest, fair, and thorough assessment.

If a patient has been detained against his will ('certified' in old nomenclature -'sectioned' in modern) he has the right of appeal to an independent body called the Mental Health Review Tribunal. This consists of a lawyer (Chairman) a doctor, usually a psychiatrist, and a lay person, chosen from a pool of people who have special experience in administration or social services. The members are appointed by the Lord Chancellor's office. The patient, or relative, can apply to have a compulsory order removed, by filling up a form to be sent to the tribunal. Reports are prepared and the decision is announced in writing soon after the hearing. Owing to lack of understanding of the procedures, many applications are refused,(over 80%) as patients are unaware of their rights and are not properly represented. The organisation MIND found that, if patients were properly represented, the proportion of successful applicants rose to 41%. But the problem remains in that even though the patients' status is reduced to 'informal' the probable of discharge remains as there are not enough hostels, half-way houses, or other community facilities to which such patients could be discharged.

Abuse of Psychiatry
Politics is about power, the desire and the ability of an alpha dominant per-

son to control the thoughts and behaviour of others, the betas and gammas – most of the psychiatrists patients come into the latter group. Yet all power corrupts and absolute power corrupts absolutely. In fact it may well drive a person mad, in the sense that he becomes detached from the reality of the needs and wishes of other people. He then slides into a world of make-believe where nothing and nobody matters except that his will should prevail.

The Roman Emperors Nero and especially Caligula were classical examples.

Recent dictators such as Hitler, Stalin, Pol Pot, Mao Zhe Dong, and Mugabe are examples. Psychiatrists were summoned to give a spurious legitimacy to their efforts to detain political opponents. Millions of innocent people have died as a consequence of their ruthlessness. The more ruthless the regime, the more the psychiatrists appeared to suffer from 'moral disarray' – the doctors who oversaw the death camps of Hitler or the Gulags of Stalin could surely not have slept easily in their beds.

'It is no accident that in those countries where diagnostic criteria are loosest (the Soviet Union and The United States) most of the serious cases of psychiatric abuse have been reported.' **(A. Clare** 1976)

In South Africa in 1967, during the period of apartheid, military conscripts were 'screened' for homosexuality by doctors and chaplains and were admitted to the Military Hospital in Pretoria for 'treatment' – abreaction with electric shocks. Between 1969 and 1987 about 900 men and women had gender reassignment surgery performed in Military Hospitals. They were then discharged, given new identity papers and told to cut themselves off from their families. Some died, some were discharged too early and needed further surgery, the casualty rates were high. In 1995 the Medical Association of South Africa issued a public apology for past wrongdoings.(BMJ No.7480 Dec.2004.

There are two sorts of psychiatrists, depending on their employers – He who pays the Piper calls the Tune. One sort is paid by the 'state' – that is to say, the taxpayer. The other is paid by the client or patient. Each sort has their agenda. The problem is one of control, in whose interest is the psychiatrist functioning? A classical example is that of the not uncommon case of puerperal depression. The unfortunate mother is unable to function properly, so someone else has to take over, to make decisions, assume control. In the bad old days she would be 'certified' and 'put away', relieving everyone of the embarrassment. Sometimes the husband had another female so this was quite convenient for him. The psychiatrist was engaged to carry out his wishes. Hopefully this does not happen today with modern insight, care, and effective treatment for depression.

— • —

'Over the past 50 years the National Health Service has been reasonably successful in making treatment available to all, irrespective of social power or wealth, and the advantages offered to patients by private care became increasingly invisible. These changes have been partially reversed in recent years by chronic underfunding, by the introduction of systems of management operating on assumptions derived from industry or supermarkets and involving the marginalizing of clinicians, and by an ideological shift.

The egalitarian aims of the NHS are being subverted and the UK is moving towards a situation like that in the USA, where a substantial minority of citizens enjoy health standards and health care at third world levels. In such a situation, psychotherapy, which in the case of psychoanalytic approaches has always kept one foot in the private sector, could easily become a commodity, purchasable by the well off or provided as a perk like the company car, but unavailable to the more deprived and distressed whose needs are far greater.

Borderline Personality Disorder,(see Diagnosis- Chapter 2) being persistent and severe, is likely to be particularly unpopular with private companies or health insurers, so 'treatment' of it will be left to the depleted public services. "Having developed and taught Cognitive Analytic Therapy with the precise aim of making therapy available to those in need, I find these developments obscene, and I am deeply perturbed by the passivity of the majority of psychotherapists in the face of them' (**Anthony Ryle**, 1997)

Some years ago, Sir **John Anderton**, Chief Constable of Greater Manchester Police, pointed to Strangeways jail and said 'Half of the people in there shouldn't be there, and the other half should never be let out.'

Psychiatrists are called upon to determine whether a defendant is 'mad' or 'bad' (Though it must be admitted that many of them are just stupid. It

45

is a sad reflection on our educational system that many inmates of jails are illiterate. A lad who is unable to read a 'keep off the grass' notice – both sorts – is in trouble from the outset). If they are diagnosed as 'mad', they are sent to Special Hospitals such as Broadmoor, Ashurst formerly Rampton, or Moss Side. If 'bad', they are sent to jail on conviction. Unfortunately life is not as simple as this, as it depends on the availability of 'places'. With the closure of many large psychiatric institutions, 'community care' is offered, with a varying degree of success, and the victims become 'homeless', until they commit an offence and are put back in prison. A sad reflection on the way we in the UK treat our weakest citizens is the fact that we incarcerate as a percentage more people than any other country in Europe. (The USA is even worse). Recently one of the criteria for admission to a secure hospital was the concept of 'treatability'. If they were considered untreatable, they would not be admitted – a very dubious attitude. Psychiatrists were reluctant to accept responsibility for the actions of their patients, understandably.

— • —

For purposes of description it can be said that animals communicate at three levels – the instinctive, the emotional and, in the case of Man, the intellectual, meaning words, thought and speech. With the evolution of writing, communication has become more precise and focussed.

Psychiatrists investigate, analyse, understand and hopefully help to restore disorders of behaviour and communication. The concept of happiness is something else, and perhaps arises when adaptation is achieved, biologically. It cannot be obtained by medication, in spite of the hopes and claims of the drug firms.

Today, as we look back 100 years, we are amazed at the activity, attitude, and ideas prevalent at the time. No doubt 100 years from now, people will look back equally amazed at our ideas and attitudes. (Evidence-based medicine – one cannot be objective about the subjective).

CHAPTER THREE

DIAGNOSIS

Words have to be coined to describe constellations of symptoms and signs to provide evidence of a disordered or pathological state, and for classification. (DSM – IV describes over 300 'diagnoses'). There is little problem when the condition is 'organic' 'physical' such as stroke, coronary thrombosis, appendicitis, (though there will always be emotional overtones with every condition). But diagnostic entities dissolve with non-physical conditions, that is to say, patients concerning whom there is no evidence of organic pathology, but manifested by anxiety, behaviour disorder, thought disorder, and communication disorder. We must note 'Occam's Razor' – *Entities are not to be Multiplied beyond Necessity*.

'Psychiatrists lay great weight on 'diagnosis'. This indicated the illness or disorder which they should treat, and was a judgement which only they could make, or change; it was one which increased in value during the 1970s with the rise of biological psychiatry. But 'diagnosis' was much less significant in the assessment of patients for rehabilitation. **Eugen Bleuler** stressed the importance of keeping in touch with the person behind the psychosis. It was found that only 'domestic skills' predicted outcome for survival outside hospital.

Yet diagnostic accuracy is necessary to provide appropriate management, treatment and particularly, prognosis. If science is an adventure at the frontier of uncertainty, then the more scientific, in the sense of rational, the better. In addition, in a fraught emotional situation, a 'diagnosis' can help to raise the situation from an emotional level to an intellectual one, thereby helping to a rational resolution of the problem.

Abortion

(This is not strictly a diagnosis, more a psychiatric emergency when inadvertent pregnancy is diagnosed). The word is currently used to mean an induced termination of pregnancy, as opposed to 'miscarriage' meaning a spontaneous termination.

A BRIEF HISTORY OF PSYCHIATRY

Psychiatrists are called upon to evaluate the mental state, especially with regard to suicide, of the patient, in order to sign the 'green form' authorising the termination of the pregnancy. Psychiatrists are put in an invidious position.

For many years, centuries in fact, pregnancy termination was considered immoral (it still is – is not the preservation of life the ethical basis of medical practice?) and was illegal. The Hippocratic oath forbids it. It was one of the five 'As' for which a doctor could be struck off the medical register and deprived of his livelihood. (The others are Alcohol, Adultery, Advertising, and Associating with unregistered practitioners).

A girl with cash and connections could be relieved of her embarrassment safely, though illegally, so why could not any girl, ran the argument. Illegal abortions were fraught with hazard from haemorrhage and infection and many girls died. So in 1967 the Medical Termination of Pregnancy Act was passed by which a girl could be assessed by two doctors, one of whom was a psychiatrist, to testify that her mental health was more likely to be impaired if the pregnancy was allowed to continue than if it were terminated. This of course is somewhat ambiguous- a 'cop out' in modern terminology. Who can predict the future? Unfortunately many girls bitterly regret their termination later in life. But it has led to the legal termination of 186,000 pregnancies in 2003 in the NHS, one of the commonest operations performed. (In the USA it is 1.3 million per annum) – a sad reflection on the inadequacy of sex education , which concentrates too much on the physical side (use a condom!) to the exclusion of the emotional. Apparently the Dutch practice is much better as their termination rate is said to be about a fifth of the British. Also, sadly, termination of pregnancy all too frequently leads to subsequent infertility. The figure of 30% has been quoted. Yet:

Better, Oh Better, to cancel from the scroll
Of Universe, one luckless human Soul,
Than enlarge the flood that grows
Hoarser with anguish, as the ages roll.
The Rubaiyat of Omar Khayyam

(Better, oh better, to delete all reference to pregnancy termination from the Statutes and leave the matter to the consciences of those concerned. There is no place for a policeman in the consulting room or the operating Theatre).

Addiction

In 1981 **Bruce Alexander**, Ph.D. **Robert Coambs** and **Patricia Hadaway** of the Department of Psychology, Simon Fraser University, Vancouver, Canada, decided to test the theory that Drug Addiction was a Cultural not a Chemical phenomenon.

To this end, they constructed a Rat Park, a 200 square foot housing colony for their white Wister rats, male and female, complete with cedar wood shavings, bright balls, wheels and tin cans. There was ample space for mating, birthing, and warm nests for lactating females. Everything that would keep a rat happy, in fact.

16 rats were put in the Park, another 16 in Cages. In addition to food, both sets were given the opportunity to drink either plain water or water laced with sweetened morphine. After 57 days the findings were as follows.

Caged rats consumed increasing doses of the morphine mixture. Park ('free') rats resisted the morphine, preferring plain water. No matter how sweet the solution was (rats love sugar) they still preferred water. When the morphine antagonist naloxone was added to the solution, the free rats did not mind drinking the solution, even though it contained morphine.

The inference is that rats, normally curious and gregarious, are extremely stressed by being confined, and find relief in 'drugs'. Also, the free rats found the sedative effect of morphine unpleasant and inhibiting.

In another experiment, both free and caged rats were denied plain water. The free rats became addicted to morphine, but when plain water was substituted, they preferred the water, suggesting that addiction is reversible.

Unfortunately, neither 'Science' nor 'Nature' would publish this research and Dr Alexander lost his research funding, and the Park closed down on the grounds that ventilation was inadequate. However, the Park was reopened shortly after for a student counselling service. The ventilation was clearly adequate for people, not for rats. The methodology could be criticized on the grounds that the 'free' rats were not living in a 'real' world, with its shortages, its conflicts, not to mention rat poison, but in a rat utopia, an ideal world that does not exist.

Alexander concluded that addiction is a consequence of 1. Availability, 2 Dislocation. It is a life-style strategy, a response to unbearable stress, but malleable to diversion and opportunity.

'Science' today insists on 'objectivity', 'evidence' and only molecular biologists get funded.

Addiction is a state of periodic or persistent intoxication, detrimental to the individual and to society.

1. There is a very powerful compulsion to continue taking the drug.
2. Physical and emotional dependence occurs.
3. Tolerance develops, and an increasing dose is required to obtain the desired effect.
4. Very unpleasant withdrawal symptoms occur if the drug is unobtainable or withheld.

Addiction often starts in youth, mostly caused by a disturbed infancy and childhood, abuse and neglect, an inability to make proper relationships, a loss of the sense of reality and identity, they don't know where they belong.(*To belong* is one of the four instinctive imperatives common to all social animals. The others are to *create*, to *communicate* and to *explore*). Often it starts at 15, becomes a problem at 17, by 22, seeking help. By 28 rock bottom, perhaps due to the death of a partner. Addicts feel inadequate, unable to cope, but, with a fix, they feel warm and secure. Narcotics Anonymous is a self help organization similar to Alcoholics Anonymous, which can help. Properly regulated clinics, assessments of need, and judicious prescribing, is one answer. The trouble is that addicts become liars – the only drug that does not seem to have this effect is nicotine. A person will be quite truthful about the number of cigarettes he or she smokes, but medical students are told to double the amount a man says he drinks, and treble the amount a woman says she drinks. *Methadone* substitution is used for the treatment of morphine and heroin addiction. *Naloxone* (a morphine antagonist) eye drops can establish that a person is in fact on morphine or heroin, as they will cause the pin-point pupils of the addict to dilate.

Addiction is a huge economic cost, said to be £4 Billion in 1998, including drug related crime and health costs, and had doubled over a period of 4 years. In 1999 68% of people arrested by Cambridge police tested positive for illegal drugs. 51% of people awaiting trial were *dependent* on drugs. The prison population is awash with drugs, perhaps condoned by the governor, as it makes for a quiet life. Swedish studies suggest that involvement in a rehabilitation programme dramatically reduces the death rate from heroin users, provided that they have not already got AIDS. Perhaps there is something to be said for the nuclear family, where identity is not uncertain, and relationships are not fraught.

Management of addiction is complex, commencing with detoxication followed by some form of cognitive analytic or behaviour therapy to prevent recurrence. But people must not be sent for therapy by the Courts as this associates therapy with punishment which is quite inappropriate.

In 2002 the Home Office British Crime Survey estimated there were up to 67,000 people in Britain using heroin. Unofficial estimates put the figure up to half a million. There is no consensus as to the correct approach. Until the epidemic started in 1960, Britain took a tolerant attitude to heroin addiction. They were registered, able to get their prescriptions from their GP, and carried on with their lives, with no harassment to withdraw or abstain. In 1968 there were less than 2000 registered addicts. In 1968 this practice was abolished, to be replaced by Drug Dependency Units, under the NHS, supervised by consultant psychiatrists. By the 1970s and 1980s the epidemic had spiralled and prescribing heroin was phased out, to be replaced by the American model of prescribing oral methadone with a view to rapid reduction and abstinence. In spite of this method being deeply flawed, it was orthodox for 20 years. In one study only 40% of those who entered the programme were drug free after 5 years. The trouble was that methadone was even more addictive than heroin, and withdrawal symptoms even worse, and patients turned to the black market for supplies. In the NHS clinics patients were treated like criminals and social outcasts, and liars, which some of them were, as a consequence of their mismanagement. In 1999 it was realised that 'reduction and abstinence' was a failure and that maintenance was preferable in some cases.

Due to the failure of the reduction and abstinence philosophy in the 1980s private clinics became established to prescribe for those patients that had been rejected by the NHS. The Stapleford Cinic was set up in Harley Street by **Dr Colin Brewer**, to help patients who had been under **Dr Ann Dalley**, who had been prosecuted for 'irregular prescribing'. Dr Brewer offered an out patient service, so that, by prescribing a regular dose, his patients could 'get on with their lives'.(50% of his patients were on injectables, compared with 10% in NHS clinics. Brewer's philosophy was that addiction treatment unit should be more like family planning clinics. 'You

51

do not go to a family planning Clinic to be told that you can have the pill and nothing else. Everybody who goes to a family planning clinic knows broadly why they are there and you can discuss sensibly with the staff a range of options. Addiction treatment has to be like that.' Health Department 'Guidelines' said that patients must be prescribed on a daily basis and medication to be consumed on the premises, to prevent diversion to the black market. (But 72% of the Stapleford patients were either working or in college education). Dr Brewers' method was so successful that more clinics were opened and have treated more than 4000 patients over the years, and he has 300 maintenance patients on his books. Unfortunately, Dr Brewer has fallen foul of the medical establishment in the person of **Dr John Strang**.

Dr Brewer advocated the use of *Naltrexone*, ('psychiatry's most effective drug' – according to Dr Brewer) a morphine antagonist, which blocks receptor sites for morphine or heroin in the brain. The technique makes relapse 'virtually impossible'. Oral treatment only lasts 3 days, but an implant can be effective for 5 weeks to 6 months. But withdrawal symptoms means that it should only be done in a hospital situation. And it does not address the psychological problems that under-pin addiction, to be addressed by therapy and counselling. Unfortunately a patient died in August 2002 under home detoxication due to inhalation of vomit. Dr Brewer and several of his colleagues have been referred to the General Medical Council on account of alleged over-prescribing. In 2005 the GMC commenced proceedings.

Addiction treatment centers must be more like hospitals than chemists' shops, with a clinical atmosphere, and unsupervised injecting will be increasingly unacceptable to the client.

In May 2001 a Government-funded Medically Supervised Injecting Centre was established in the King's Cross area of Sydney, Australia supervised by the Medical Director, **Dr Ingrid van Beek**, a public health and addiction medicine physician, in spite of opposition ranging from the Vatican to the UN International Narcotics Control Board. A licence was issued by the NSW police and health departments. It was to target the homeless and socially excluded. In its first 18 months there were 3818 users with 50,000 injecting episodes. There were 429 overdoses without fatality, including 329 heroin, 80 cocaine, 20 benzodiazepine overdoses. The licence to operate has been extended to 2007.

The Drugs trade is a classical example of the exploitation of human misery by the unscrupulous. There is much to be said for de-criminalisation of cannabis and to levy a tax, similar to tobacco, with supplies sold by registered dealers, as with tobacco. There is some evidence that cannabis is marginally less harmful than tobacco or alcohol, and at least the purchasers would get a standard product, uncontaminated by possibly harmful by-products. Taxes could be levied, the funds being ring-fenced to provide clinics in a hospital-type setting to help heroin addicts, where they could obtain standardized supplies and to enter an abstinence programme, if they were motivated. This would remove the market forces driving the trade, with its high level of corruption, blackmail and intimidation inevitable when enormous profits are to be made. The test for good law is 'cui bono?' – To whose good?. It would appear that the only people benefitting from existing legislation are the drug barons and the dealers. Certainly the present arrangements are not working. 75% of all crime is said to be drug related and increasing numbers of people are being jailed (It costs the taxpayer £40,000 a year to keep a person in jail) with its terrible consequence on family lives and relationships.

Another consequence of the present arrangements is the break up of the family life of the addict. What happens is that the addict starts stealing money from his parents in order to finance his habit. They are reluctant to shop him to the police so this can go on for some time. However when he starts stealing from his grandparents they may well have no such scruples and 'turn him in' and he now has a criminal record. With the result that he is virtually removed from those who are most able to help him and finds himself 'on the street', and at the mercy of the dealers.

The problem of invoking the law with regard to drug addiction is that there is, in any society, a group of people who ignore the law, perhaps 1%. But 1% of 60,000,000 is 600,000. Discounting the very young and very old, this may be reduced to say, 100,000, a lot of people. If there was evidence that 'the law' would reduce the consumption of drugs, there would be something to be said for it. But even the death penalty, in some countries, has still not been much of a deterrent.

There is a certain amount of hypocrisy in those who advocate a 'crack down' on drugs, with severe penalties, as they are frequently found to consume moderate or even large quantities of that common recreational drug – alcohol – themselves.

ADHD – Attention Deficit Hyperactivity Disorder.

A popular 'diagnosis' applied to children who fail to conform to school's requirement. There are said to be 350,000 children (5% of the school population) suffering from this and receiving medication – Ritalin (methylphenidate, an amphetamine derivative.) There is no test for this condition, there is no evidence of benefit, and there is no information of any lasting harm. There is some evidence that it is a nutritional disorder due to high intake of saturated fatty acids and can be helped by EPA (omega 3) and other polyunsaturated fatty acids

Alcoholism

'First the Man takes the Drink, then the Drink takes the Man.'

The conscience is that part of the personality that is soluble in alcohol.

1. There is an insatiable desire for alcohol after a small drink which acts as a trigger.
2. There may be 'black outs', with an altered state of consciousness and memory loss.
3. Tolerance develops and increasing amounts of alcohol are needed.
4. Withdrawal symptoms occur when denied alcohol.
5. Spiritual desolation, terror, bewilderment, frustration and despair.
6. Risk of suicide.

There may be a genetic basis in some cases, as certain ethnic types seem to be more prone to this condition. Stress undoubtedly plays a very important part, particularly with unresolved conflicts. Guilt feelings lead to secret drinking. Some alcoholics appear to function normally until some factor, such as being involved in a road traffic accident, leads to investigation. Since one of the distressing symptoms of addicts is they are 'economical with the truth' they will deny their alcohol intake. They must be confronted with a fasting blood alcohol level to make them realize that they must face the facts. The blood alcohol level is measured, and found to be unacceptably high, and hopefully they will seek treatment. Since abstinence causes unpleasant withdrawal symptoms, these can be mitigated by administration of diazepam 20 mgm daily, initially, gradually reduced over a period of days or weeks. They must be closely monitored.

But alcohol is a poison, and liver damage occurs leading to cirrhosis. The central nervous system is damaged, leading possibly to brain failure.

Delirium tremens is a complication, not only of high alcohol levels, but of withdrawal. The patient is tense, anxious, with coarse tremor , delusions and hallucinations, often visual (pink elephants) or cutaneous, insects crawling over the skin (formication). Auditory hallucinations are often abusive and frightening and the patient seeks refuge. Insomnia occurs, sometimes epileptic fits (10%). Paranoid delusions especially of jealousy and infidelity are directed towards a wife.

Korsakoff's psychosis is a late development of alcoholism The patient becomes confused, disorientated, paranoid, and confabulates, meaning giving ready answers and reciting experiences with total disregard of the truth – in a word – lying, due to loss of memory for recent events. Acute alcoholic intoxication needs hospital admission. Intravenous fluids may be necessary, with phenothiazine medication to control nausea and vomiting and minimize withdrawal symptoms. Recovery may take a week or more. Thiamine and niacin vitamins must be given especially if there are neurological symptoms.

Various treatment regimes have been tried to prevent recurrence, including *aversion therapy*, in which the patient is given a drink, then an injection of *apomorphine* is given to induce nausea and vomiting. After repeated episodes, the patients develops an aversion to alcohol.

Antabuse is a drug which interferes with alcohol metabolism so that acetaldehyde is formed. This causes such an unpleasant reaction that the patient is reluctant to continue drinking. Motivation is clearly necessary for this treatment to be effective so that he continues to take the tablets.

Joining *Alcoholics Anonymous* shows motivation and helps to overcome the temptation to seek solace from the bottle. Only a recovered alcoholic knows how awful it is and can offer comfort and advice to a friend.

Alcoholism remains a serious condition. In the UK in 2001 there were said to be 5,970 alcohol related deaths, in 2003, 6,580 deaths, the true figure may be even greater. Males exceeded females by 3 to 2. Legally, deaths associated with alcoholism must be reported to the coroner, who may decide to hold an inquest, which may cause unpleasantness and distress.

Alzheimer's Disease (the term *brain failure* is preferable to *dementia*, as the latter has derogatory connotations.)

A condition described by **Dr Alois Alzheimer** in 1907. He was a neuropathologist who noted diffuse atrophy of the cerebral cortex, with neurofibrillary tangles and plaques in the brain of a 51-year old woman, who suffered from pathological jealousy, paranoia, and screaming fits, becoming more apathetic, and dying after 4 years. (A similar condition was described by **Dr Arnold Pick** in Prague, with frontal lobe atrophy).

The plaques contain a protein beta-amyloid. There is also a deficiency of the neurotransmitter acetyl choline in the brains of sufferers and cholinesterase blockers have been used in treatment.

It is characterised by memory impairment, both long and short term, impairment of thought, and personality change, in the absence of other pathological conditions such as brain tumour.

It may take 2-20 years to progress, average 5-10 years.

There may be a genetic basis for some cases.

There may be an increased level of aluminium in the brains of sufferers. Patients on renal dialysis may develop the condition due to increased levels of aluminium in the dialysis fluid.

It has been estimated that there are 500,000 sufferers in the UK and it is clearly the greatest economic and social burden on society today. Especially a financial burden on families, as a consequence of increasing longevity.

Other causes of brain failure have been described, such as multi-infarct, and there may well be others as yet to be identified. All cases of brain failure must be investigate by MRI scans exclude other potentially treatable causes such as tumour.

Anorexia Nervosa

This was originally described by Dr **William Gull** in 1868. A condition mainly confined to young women, round about the age of puberty, in affluent societies. The girl is preoccupied with her shape, thinks she is too fat in spite of evidence to the contrary. It may be due to unresolved conflict in family relationships, particularly when there are unreal expectations of her parents as to her abilities and objectives. Parents have a tendency to expect their children to be like themselves, but they are not and never will be. (Khalil Gibran thought that parents should try to be more like their children.) What happens is that the girl refuses to eat and her weight progressively falls, alarmingly. Food consumption is always a weapon young children use to annoy their parents and to achieve control, but young children do not starve themselves to death, unlike anorexics. Often the girl takes a great interest in food, and cooks for the family, but just won't eat anything. When the girl's weight reaches about 7 stone (98 pounds 45 Kg) the menstrual periods stop. Her parents then become alarmed that she might be pregnant. In fact this is the least likely scenario, as she rejects all attention, seeking it and at the same time, rejecting it. A fine downy hair may develop (similar to the baby's lanugo), but anorexics are desperate to cover themselves up.

Many cases are resolved in the family setting, and never come to the doctor's attention. If a doctor or counsellor is involved, it is important that he or she does not take sides, ideally becoming a moderator or advocate. The counsellor should be an advocate for the defence (the patient) rather than the prosecution (the parents). Weighing may not be possible at first as many girls are ashamed of their skinny hairy bodies and refuse to get undressed. Their wishes must be respected. This a condition in which the Art of Medicine is more important than the Science. Establishing eye contact is essential, in order to achieve control. Management consists in trying to improve her self-esteem, and cognitive behaviour therapy helps by correcting erroneous thought processes and ideas – 'I am too fat'. There may be an element of attention seeking in the condition – repeated weighing sometimes is counter-productive. However, it is a condition that does carry a mortality and referral for specialist help may be necessary. Special clinics have been set up to this end. Anti-depressants have been used but many girls refuse to take pills, and may indeed unhelpfully swallow the lot. The cases with the worst prognosis were those where all contact with the family had been lost, often at the instigation of the therapist. Trying to 'get to the bottom of it' may not be helpful. When they grow up they become models or social workers, and, if there has been an element of abuse in their upbringing, tend to find abuse in dysfunctional families when there may have been little or none. This may cause immense grief to otherwise united families (see also Bulimia below).

Autism (ASD) (Autism Spectrum Disorder – not to be confused with atrial septal defect)

A spectrum developmental disorder characterized by 'aloneness' and obsessive insistence on Sameness, with stereotyped repetitive movements. It was first described by **Leo Kanner** in 1943 in Baltimore, USA and independently by **Hans Asperger** in 1944 in Vienna. The label had been used by Eugen Bleuler in 1911 in a description of schizophrenia, but this description is inappropriate in autism as the clinical picture is quite different.

Asperger's syndrome has been used for the upper end of the spectrum, in which the child is highly intelligent, verbal and near normal. The condition is probably congenital, may well be due to chromosome abnormality, similar to Down's syndrome (Mongolism) where a definite chromosome abnormality has been identified (trisomy 21) but not yet in autism. It is possible that there may be a virus intra-uterine cause. Some autistic children appear to have a defective immune system, with gastrointestinal symptoms. The notion that MMR vaccine 'causes' autism is almost certainly incorrect. What appears to happen is that autism is 'triggered' by the MMR vaccine in certain susceptible children, those with the genetic defect, possibly those with elderly parents similar to Down's. Therefore there should be intense effort to locate this defect in order that it can be identified in early pregnancy (similar to Down's) so that the pregnancy can be terminated if that is the parent's wish.

There is some concordance in identical twins – 4 out of 11. It is a comparatively rare condition, various estimates range between 2 and 10 per 10,000., with boys exceeding girls by 2.5 to 1. The excess sometimes noted in children of upper social class parents may be due to referral bias, or to ageing parents.

Autistic children are sometimes very talented, musically (perfect pitch) or artistically or mathematically. But they are unable to make use of their talent, which involves relating to other people. The film 'Rainman' (starring **Dustin Hoffman**, who spent 2 years researching the part) excellently illustrates the problem. All remarks are taken literally. A nurse asked a 10 year old autistic girl, from whom she wished to obtain a blood sample – 'give me your hand'. The child screamed with fright and horror as she though the nurse was going to cut off her hand. Autistc children frequently develop epilepsy about the age of 10, signifying brain damage.

Whilst Down's syndrome babies are recognizable at birth, autistic children are not and are often very physically attractive. Previously they were assumed to be generally mentally deficient. But autistic children inhabit a lonely world, where nothing has meaning, and is very frightening. (The computer analogy is with a defective operating system, that which gives meaning to symbols. Thus, when one depresses the letter A on the keyboard, a series of marks and spaces (1s and 0s according to the ASCII code) are generated, which are then converted by the operating system to the letter A which appears on the monitor, and has meaning).

The baby does not respond normally to eye contact, cannot make relationships, and resents change. By the age of a year developmental milestones come to be missed and by the age of 3 it is becoming clear that there is a problem. They lack 'empathy'.

There is no better description of the bizarre and frightening world inhabited by a teenager with Asperger's syndrome than the book *The Curious Incident of the Dog in the Night Time* by Mark Haddon.(Vintage 2004 imprint of Random House)

— • —

An interesting analogy relating to children with communication difficulties is the story of:

The Wolf Children of Midnapore

In 1920, in India, near to the town of Midnapore, in West Bengal, about 80 miles west of Calcutta, it was reported that there were ghosts and demons and evil spirits in the jungle. The local people, the Santals, were terrified and would not go near the place where they were said to be. The Rev. Joseph Singh was the priest in charge of the local Mission and the associated orphanage. When he heard of the demons, he was determined to find out what was happening. He was told they inhabitated the base of a huge ant-hill, an abandoned termite mound. He mounted an expedition to locate them, and, together with help of another tribe – the Lodhas, who were not terrified, built a tree platform to observe what was happening. After a few days, as dusk fell, a few wolf cubs were seen emerging from their lair followed by an enraged mother wolf. The hunters were quite unable to approach the lair and they killed the wolf with their arrows. When they dug out the lair they found two creatures who appeared half wolf, half human, nestling inside together with two wolf cubs. They were quickly ensnared by nets under the direction of the Rev. Singh. Attempts to clean up these children, who were encrusted with dirt and fleas and other parasites, met with great difficulty as they were terrified of contact with water. They were unable to stand upright. One girl was assessed as being about 3 years old, the other about 5 or 6. They were wild and ferocious with blank expressions on their faces. Rev. Singh was determined to keep the circumstances of their capture secret, claiming they were the abandoned children of mendicant fakirs, in order to allay curiosity. They were kept in a compound. At first they would only drink milk and water. They got around on elbows(or hands) and knees. They made friends with the local dogs and would eat their food, meat, offal and bones. They tore off any clothes that were put on them. The younger was called Amala, the elder, Kamala, and photographs were taken. They were terrified of being put into the light, and howled in the darkness, never sleeping after midnight. They urinated and defaecated wherever they were. They were encouraged to associate with puppies and the younger children at the orphanage. After about 2 months, a little boy called Benjamin of about a year old went up to them, unseen by Mrs Singh, and was tolerated. But after about 10 days of fraternisation, the wolf children turned on him and savaged him, rescued just in time by Mrs. Singh. After about 4 months,the younger girl Amala would make a sound like 'bhoo' for water. Soon after, they began to look at Mrs Singh and run to her when distressed. She had been talking to the other children with Amala and Kamala in earshot. Mrs Singh started to treat them like other children, offering food as a reward for good behaviour. It appeared that the younger child Amala learned faster than Kamala.

In September 1921, about 10 months after their capture, Amala fell seriously ill with dysentery. Rev Singh was forced to call a local doctor, Dr Sarbadhicari, who was a notorious gossip, and she was treated with sulphur, which caused the expulsion of a large quantity of roundworms.She was also suffering from nephritis and died a few days later, shortly after Rev Singh had baptized her. Kemala appeared extremely distraught, and went into a trance like state, verging on the catatonic, for several weeks. The story of the wolf children then became public, and had to be seen by locals, much to Rev. Singh's displeasure as he did not want Kemala to be treated as a freak but to lead as normal a life as possible. Mrs. Singh began working on her, massaging her limbs to try to straightening them out and talking to her all the time, and she began to associate with the other orphanage children. By putting her food, she still preferred raw meat, on a table, she eventually got her to stand upright and eventually to walk upright. By constant repetition, she eventually recognised her name, and could speak a few words in pidgin Bengali. She was only attached to Mrs. Singh, and became unresponsive if she went away, and would not attach herself to anyone else.

On Sept. 29th, 1929 Kemala fell ill with typhoid fever, and in spite of various treatments, she died on November 13th . During her illness she had made considerable gains in her language. She could not only talk, wrote Rev Singh, .but talk with the full sense of the words used by her. She was buried the following day next to Amala, under the Banyan tree in St. John's cemetery.

Rev. Singh wrote ' it is only possible to change a person if you can create a liking in them for the change so desired. To create a liking means you must make them understand that you are their well-wishers and you love them sincerely. Their understanding then turns from aversion to friendliness. As they grow in this knowledge they grow in that relationship of attachment. This knowledge expels the distrust which alone stands as a great demon, to destroy the incoming awakenings of all the finer feelings, and this cruelly blocks all doors of learning.'

Rev. Singh regarded the children as lost souls, and sought salvation for them, and to return them to the human race, rather than interesting specimens to be analysed, or even freaks to be gawped at. It was this motivation that led to his moderate success with exceedingly unpromising material. They started off believing they were wolves, ending up believing they were children. It would appear that the children were neither autistic nor backward as they would never have been able to adapt and survive in a den of wolves. Adapt or Perish is one of the Laws of Biology.

There have been other instances of wolf-children, of which Romulus and Remus, the founders of Rome, are perhaps the best known.

It appears that wolves have a matriarchial society, in which only the dominant female can reproduce. So there are many 'aunts' who are keen to have cubs and will pick up, rather than eat, any babies that they happen to find. Sometimes the babies are 'stolen', sometimes, particularly females, put out to take their chances in the wild.

There is no cure for autism, any more than there is for Down's syndrome. But the children respond to love, and kindness and like all education, to a firm, calm, and reassuring approach. Medication has little place in autism, apart from control of epilepsy, any more than it does for Down's syndrome.

Naloxone, a morphine antagonist, used to treat patients with morphine or heroin overdose, has been used in the treatment of autism. Theory is that autistic behaviour is due to the brain being saturated with morphine-like substances called endorphins, and that naloxone blocks this. A small percentage of children given naloxone show reduction in stereotyped behaviour and are able to interact with the world and with their 'colony'.

Borderline Personality Disorder. (BHP) (also see below – personality disorder)

'Two persons in one body. – one day laughing, so gay that any stranger seeing her at home will sing her praises: 'never so sweet in all the world, so lovable. Let a day pass and she is insufferable to come near to or look at: in a frenzy like a bitch with puppies, snapping at everyone, to friend and foe a universal shrew.' **Simonides (BC 600)**. Their personality is said to be superficially intact but deeply chaotic, with a fragmented sense of identity.

A further six qualities could be added:

1. Frantic efforts to avoid abandonment.
2. Identity disturbance.
3. Impulsiveness.
4. Suicidal and self mutilating behaviour.
5. Chronic feelings of emptiness.
6. Transient stress-related paranoid ideas and dissociative symptoms.

Whilst there is a genetic basis for all conditions, in BHP there is nearly always a history of childhood abuse, whether actively or by neglect, physical or psychological. There is difficulty in making proper relationships, and such relationships can be fraught, and violent. There is a strong tendency to self-destructive, anti-social or suicidal behaviour and drug addiction. On this account they are sometimes referred for counselling, and therapy such as cognitive behaviour or cognitive analytic. (see under Chapter 3 – Therapy) But there is a risk of suicide in these patients, estimated at 10% long term.

Bulimia

A condition related to Anorexia Nervosa, in which a girl eats ferocially (binges) and then makes herself sick. It is often associated with some form of personality disorder, going back to early childhood and poor early relationships. Treatment is difficult owing to denial and lack of cooperation, but the patient may make herself seriously ill by virtue of electrolyte imbalance. When acid is lost from the stomach during vomiting, metabolic alkalosis can occur which requires hospital admission and treatment with intravenous fluids.

Child Abuse

Soul Murder. Killing the Joy in Life and interfering with the sense of Reality. This is not new.

> *...and Jesus called a little child unto him, and set him in the midst of them... And said... But whosoever shall offend one of these little ones... it were better for him.. that a millstone were hanged about his neck and he were drowned in the depth of the sea.*
>
> (Matthew 18, v 2 & 6)

The early formative years are crucial in the development of the personality, especially the ability to form proper relationships. The ages from one to three are particularly important in that the child needs to relate to one particular person – to find a 'Guardian Angel' to whom he or she can turn in times of grief or distress, in a word – to love and be loved. In the absence of such an individual, mother or other, the personality remains undeveloped and relationships are fraught with anxiety and uncertainty, and the concept of truth remains a problem. Some people can lie with greater conviction than others can tell the truth. Such people may later be diagnosed as suffering from personality disorder.

Later on, a vulnerable person can be the victim of abuse and to be unable to make proper relationships with others, particularly sexual. Too often such people find solace in drugs. It is said that 80% of prostitutes are drug abusers – they need to go on 'the game' so as to finance their habit. They often end up in jail, such is society's total lack of understanding of the nature of their predicament.

Many abused children are led to believe that the trouble is their fault. 'You are a wicked boy' a lad is informed merely for doing what a 3 year old would do. Later, sexually abused children are told never to tell what had happened, on pain of punishment or even death. Small wonder that their personalities remain confused.

Some people have 'love' and 'hate' tattooed on their fingers. Perhaps this is an indication of loss of a sense of identity, without which the world is violent, and ultimately, meaningless (see also paraphilia below).

Unfortunately the brain has neither a 'delete' button nor an 'erase' button. Would that it had. The situation has been expressed more elegantly, succinctly and poetically by old Omar Khayyam:

> *The moving finger writes and having writ,*
> *Moves on.*
> *Nor all thy piety nor wit*
> *Can call it back to alter half a line.*
> *Nor all thy tears wash out a word of it.*

It is a terrible indictment of a society in which 2,300 calls are made *daily* to the free telephone helpline Childline. (BMJ May 2005) There must be many unhappy children about, perhaps due to the breakdown of the nuclear family and the emergence of the 'single parent family'. Stepchildren often have a hard time from their step-parents and siblings. (Cinderella Syndrome)

Chorea

This is characterized by involuntary movements of a shaking jerking or writhing nature.

Huntington's chorea was described by the American physician Dr **G.S. Huntington** (1862-1927). This in an autosomal dominant genetic disorder due to a mutation at the distal end of the short arm of chromosome 4. The prevalence is said to be 1 in 20,000. If a parent carried this, there is a 50% chance of a child being affected. Symptoms develop in adolescence or later, with progressive incoordination leading to brain failure and death after a few years. There is general cerebral atrophy with loss of neurones in the basal ganglia, which is the region of the brain responsible for coordinating reflex activity. If parents are suspected carriers, karyotyping of the foetus can be performed in early pregnancy, and, if the parents are willing, the pregnancy can be terminated.

Sydenham's chorea (St Vitus' Dance). In 1686 **Thomas Sydenham** described this disorder in children following rheumatic fever. The onset is usually gradual, with irritability, insolence, inattentativeness and fidgety movements. It may recur during pregnancy (*chorea gravidarum*) or in those taking oral contraceptives. Recovery takes place within weeks or months. It is very uncommon today as rheumatic fever is very uncommon.

Other conditions characterized by tremor and shaking are:

Parkinson's disease (described by Dr **James Parkinson** in 1817) is due to depletion of dopamine in the substantia nigra in the medulla of the brain stem, and the corpus striatum of the basal ganglia. Treatment with L-DOPA relieves the symptoms of muscular rigidity and tremor.

Multiple (disseminated) sclerosis due to areas of demyelination appearing in the brain and spinal cord of unknown cause.These can be demonstrated in an MRI scan. It has a geographical distribution, being rare at the equator and more common as one approaches higher latitudes, especially in the North.

Tardive dyskinesia is an unwelcome side effect of phenothiazine antipsychotics.

Chronic Fatigue Syndrome CFS (ME)

A condition characterized by feelings of lassitude and ill-health, without specific pathological findings. The Center for Disease Control in 1994 said that, to merit a diagnosis of CFS, patients had to suffer severe chronic fatigue for 6 months or longer, with other medical conditions excluded (normal blood count, ESR, thyroid function) and to have 4 or more of the following symptoms:

1. Substantial impairment of short term memory or concentration.
2. Sore throat.
3. Tender lymph nodes.
4. Muscle pains.

5. Multijoint pain without swelling or redness.
6. Headaches of a new type, pattern or severity.
7. Unrefreshing sleep
8. Postexertional malaise lasting more than 24 hours.

Using these criteria, a study in 2003 found that only a third of patients with chronic fatigue met the diagnostic criteria of suffering from chronic fatigue syndrome. It was also found that those suffering from CFS were more likely to be unemployed, (27%) to be in a self help group (20%) and to have concomitant depression (48%). Half of all patients attributed their fatigue to psychological stress. (*Br. J. Gen Practice – A Diagnostic Study in UK Primary Care*)

ME stands for Myalgic Encephalomyelitis. *Myalgia* means muscle pains. *Encephalomyelitis* means inflammation of the brain and spinal cord, of which there is no evidence. Muscle pains may or may not be present. It is a condition which causes much aggravation, as to whether it is a 'physical' disease.

It is certainly big business. In January 2004 £8 million was allocated by the UK Government to set up a dozen specialist centres to help people suffering from the syndrome. It was said to cost £3.6 billion per year in treatment, benefits and lost income.

It appears that milder cases suffer from loss of emotional energy or Chi (qi), and find alternative therapies helpful. A popular method of treatment is 'cognitive behaviour therapy.' (see Chapter 3).

But undoubtedly there are many who feel tired and ill following a virus illness, of which Infectious Mononucleosis (Glandular Fever) due to the Epstein-Barr virus, is perhaps the best known. Influenza is another. So the matter remains unresolved. Unfortunately ME sufferers are unable to accept that there are many uncertainties in this life. In 2003, 25,000 children (10-18 age group) were said to be affected by ME. There may be some degree of familial incidence.

Depression. Manic Depressive illness (Bipolar), Melancholia

Classically, there are two types of depression, endogenous and exogenous (reactive).

Additionally, there are two types of response to depression, the agitated and the retarded, depending on the personality type. Age of onset is commonly 50-60 years. The agitated depressive paces up and down wringing his or her hands and is convinced that nothing can be done to help. Suicide is a real risk and hospital admission is essential, under Section, where they can be treated with anti-depressants and if necessary ECT. The retarded depressive initially loses his ability to concentrate, loses interest in everything, neglects his appearance, imagines he has serious illness, delusions of cancer, finally lies inertly in bed, has to be fed, cannot be persuaded to get up, and hospital admission will be necessary (*melancholia*).

Early morning waking is characteristic of the early stages of depression. There is some evidence that depression is commoner in Northern latitudes, and in winter (SAD – Seasonal Affective Disorder) – 'they don't have depression in Nigeria'.

Prior to the mid-twentieth century, depression was seldom diagnosed, unhappy people who presented to the doctor were diagnosed as neurasthenic or neurotic. With the discovery and intense marketing of the 'anti-depressants' there developed an epidemic of 'depression'.(see psychopharmacology Chapter 4) with huge profits accruing to the drug companies and their shareholders. Perhaps it is too easy to label someone as depressed when they are just unhappy.

It can be difficult to distinguish between anxiety and depression, the two often go together, one leads to the other, and sedatives (anti-anxiety such as barbiturates and benzodiazepines, even alcohol) are often as effective in depression as anxiety. But there can be a tendency to addiction if not monitored carefully. Never should repeat prescriptions be handed out without proper review of the patient, with a view to getting them off their medication.

Bipolar (Manic depression) or *unipolar* depression without mania or mania without depression is a seriously disabling condition with a mortality from suicide. There may be a genetic or hereditary basis in many cases – defect on chromosome 11. There is usually a cyclical incidence of breakdown, occurring every 3-9 months, if untreated. In the past episodes of melancholia could last a year or more.

Mania, in which the patient is restless, elated, over-confident, full of grand ideas, spending money he has not got, buying things he does not need, working all the hours of day and night, making a thorough nuisance of himself, may well need hospital admission. Acute Mania in which the patient suffers from delusions, will certainly require admission. Chlorpromazine, haloperidol or other phenothiazine derivatives may be used.

The discovery of the beneficial effect of *lithium* prophylactically has revolutionized the treatment of bipolar illness, and the lives of many have been greatly helped. Therapy needs to be continuous, with close monitoring of the blood lithium levels, as lithium is quite toxic to the kidneys. Patients need to be warned not to discontinue the tablets even though they may feel exceedingly well. (see Chapter 4 psychopharmacology).

Many women feel low and tearful after childbirth, said to occur in 30%, perhaps a consequence of excessive anxiety during pregnancy, their emotional batteries have run down. But sometimes post-partum depression becomes pathological (1 in 1,000) and infanticide or suicide is possible. This often occurs within 6 weeks of birth, with a peak incidence 7-20 days post partum. A psychotic reaction necessitates urgent admission to hospital and treatment with phenothiazine anti-psychotics, possibly ECT. Patients may need to stay in hospital for 4-6 months, as opposed to the average 2.2 months for all admissions. A woman who has had a post-partum breakdown may subsequently suffer from pre-menstrual tension, necessitating progesterone treatment. It seems likely that there is a hormonal basis for these conditions. *Sheehan's syndrome*- pan hypo pituitarism, is a rare complication following childbirth, in which there is infarction of the pituitary gland leading to failure of lactation, myxoedema, adrenal failure, alopecia and pallor – the alabaster skin – if long standing.

Various herbal remedies have been advocated for depression, including St John's Wort (Hypericum) in a dose of 900-1800 milligrams per day.

Also polyunsaturated fatty acids such as the omega 3 EPA in a dose of 2.0 grams per day. (see Appendix 1).

Munchausen Syndrome

This was described in 1951 by **Dr Richard Asher**, consultant physician, whose claim to fame lies in the fact that he was the father of Jane Asher, Celebrity, Ex-Beatle Groupie, Actress, Film Star, Cake maker, President of the National Autistic Society.

A BRIEF HISTORY OF PSYCHIATRY

Baron von Munchausen was a character, possibly fictional, whose life was described in a book by R.E.Raspe (1775). He was a compulsive liar, claimed to be widely travelled, and to have met many famous people, telling stories that are both dramatic and untruthful, usually with a military or services background, with many 'triumphs', largely fictitious.

1. Patients with this condition have a multiplicity of scars, often abdominal.
2. They show a mixture of truculence and evasiveness in their manner.
3. Their history is acute and harrowing, yet not entirely convincing. Excruciating abdominal pain is unaccompanied by corresponding physical signs. Alleged catastrophic blood loss is unaccompanied by pallor or anaemia.-
4. A. wallet or handbag stuffed with hospital attendance cards, insurance claim forms, and litigious correspondence. Unfortunately, they often have a real organic lesion, so the physician must be very wary. (The syndrome of the clenched fist). Several typical cases are mentioned in Dr Asher's book *Talking Sense*, Pitman Medical 1972. First mentioned in the Lancet of 10 February 1951).

A more recent variant of Munchausen syndrome is that of female patients pretending to have a family history of breast cancer so as to receive breast operations and hence much sympathy. They forbid doctors to contact the family. (Mentioned in brackets – Munchausen syndrome by Proxy. A condition described by the controversial paediatrician Sir Roy Meadows. It was to give a name to a curious behaviour disorder of mothers who are said to – 'invent illnesses in, and sometimes harm, their children.' This 'diagnosis' was used to accuse mothers of murdering children who had suffered cot death for whatever reason. There were many gross miscarriages of justice as the mothers were found guilty of murder and wrongfully imprisoned. It is quite clear that a woman who kills her child, if in fact she has, is suffering from a serious mental disorder and requires help and treatment rather than punishment.

Mutism Mute of Malice or Mute of the Will of God say the lawyers.

'Give Sorrow Words: the Grief that does not Speak
whispers the o'er fraught Heart and bids it Break'

Thus spake Malcolm, son of Duncan, King of Scotland, to Macduff, on being told that his wife and children had been murdered by MacBeth. In The Scottish play. (MacBeth Act IV scene 3) by William Shakespeare.

Aphonia is the subjective 'functional' non-physical condition, to be distinguished from *aphasia*, which is organic, due to brain damage such as from senility or stroke, affecting the speech center, Broca's area, situated in the inferior frontal gyrus of the left frontal lobe of the brain in right handed people, in the right frontal lobe in left handed people. *Nominal aphasia* is the inability to recall proper nouns, called 'senior moments' by senior citizens.

Elective Mutism. Mutism from shock, especially in children.

Selective mutism. 'I'll never speak to you again if you do/don't do this that or the other.' Or even for no reason at all. The angry silence. 'Sent to Coventry'. An indication of displeasure, whereby the dominant individual or group excludes the subordinate one.

Deaf-mutes are those unfortunate individuals who are unable to speak because their hearing is so impaired that they have never heard the spoken word in infancy, thus their brain has never been 'programmed'. If recognized, they can often be taught to speak, or alternatively to use a sign language.

Obsessive Compulsive disorder (OCD)

Obsessions are recurrent or persistent irrational thoughts, images, or impulses that arise spontaneously independently of volition. They may be shameful, repugnant, merely tedious, often meaningless and are accompanied by anxiety. There may be worries about contamination and fear of committing violent acts.

Compulsions are said to be associated with obsessions in 80% of cases. They are impulses to commit repetitive acts that are apparently meaningless, stereotyped or ritualistic, such as repetitive hand washing, counting, checking that stoves have been switched off, and repeating stereotyped words or phrases. Sometimes it is necessary to perform elaborate rituals, which the sufferer knows are meaningless but experiences great anxiety if they are not performed.

The drugs *clomipramine* (*anafranil*) and *fluoxetine* (*prozac*) have been used effectively in the treatment of this condition. When all else has failed and the patients' life and family are totally disrupted by their compulsions, leucotomy may be done. Recently, group therapy has been advocated.

But mild obsessionals make excellent book keepers, actuaries and accountants.

An interesting variant of OCD is *Tourette's syndrome*. One of the first cases to be described was a French noblewoman, the Marquise de Dampierre. She shocked her family by her strange behaviour when she would compulsively shout out 'shit and fucking pig.' She was described by J.M.G. Itard in Paris and later by **Georges Gilles de la Tourette** 60 years later. He collected a series of cases and realised that it had the hallmarks of a syndrome. It is a hereditary neuro-behavioural disorder characterized by motor tics, compulsive behaviour and involuntary vocalizations, often of an obscene nature, but including spitting, coughing, barking, blowing or whistling. Symptoms often appear between 8-12 years of age, and manifestations tend to wax and wane, sometimes disappearing. It is more common in boys and Ashkenazi Jews. The Roman Emperor Claudius was a victim, and they are usually of normal intelligence and often successful in their chosen field by virtue of their obsessive nature. They can be helped by drugs as above.

Paraphilia

These are sexual perversions or deviations of the sexual act or the sexual object.

1. Fetishism. Inanimate objects are the means of sexual arousal.
2. Transvestism. Men wearing clothes of the opposite sex as a means of sexual arousal.
3. Zoophilia. Bestiality. Animals are used as sexual objects.
4. Paedophilia. Children are the victims of sexual abuse.
5. Exhibitionism. Exposure of the male genitals to unsuspecting females is used to obtain sexual gratification.
6. Others includes sadism, masochism, voyeurism.

Treatment of these conditions is generally unsatisfactory owing to absence of motivation. They are referred by the Courts as nobody knows what to do. Oestrogen implants have been used to diminish sexual libido. Paedophiles are generally imprisoned.

Parents have an obligation to protect their children from the attentions of pederasts. This is being increasingly difficult due to 'chat rooms' on the internet.

Personality Disorder (To be distinguished from Borderline Personality Disorder).

The virus of violence has entered the soul of the psychopath. The psychopathic personality is someone who appears to have no conscience, lacks empathy and commits the most horrifying crimes with no sign of remorse or regret. Disputes and arguments are met, not by reason, but by violence. There is, as with everything, a genetic basis for this, but in addition, often a history of abuse and neglect in early childhood. They are frequently compulsive liars (some people can lie more convincingly than others can tell the truth) cheats and cowards and become the playgound bullies if they ever go to school. They become the politicians, tycoons, war lords and dictators (Stalin, Hitler, Pol Pot etc.etc.) later in life. Frequently they have an ingratiating smile (the smile on the face of the tiger) and can inspire great affection. It can be difficult to know who is more terrified of them, their followers or their enemies. Sometimes they get found out (Enron and Worldcom), sometimes becoming alcoholic or drug addicts or committing suicide to escape the humiliation of justice. When in jail, they can dominate the organization by threats and intimidation. It has recently been rediscovered that violent and aggressive behaviour can be reduced by proper nutrition.

It has been said that the psychological profile of some international conglomerates is that of the psychopath. Genocide occurs when a nation becomes infected by psychopathy.

Some nations behave pyschopathically and fail to observe the foundation of all morality and ethics – *the end does not justify the means* – and indulge in pre-emptive strikes.

The cause of personality disorder is multifactorial.
1. Genetic, as with everything.
2. Brain damage.

3. Malnutrition.
4. Abuse or neglect in childhood.
5. Drugs.

There is little research evidence that 'treatment ' of psychopathy is effective, either in terms of individual mental health or of public safety.

The median length of stay in Broadmoor Special Hospital is said to be 6.3 years. XYY karyotype (see chap 7 intersex) was found in 3% of abnormally aggressive patients in a maximum security hospital
Aggression tends to diminish after the age of 45.

Phobic Anxiety State (Social Anxiety state)

Fear is the emotional response to a perceived real and imminent threat to life. Such as coming face to face with a tiger while walking in the jungle. Or, more likely, having a loaded gun pointed at one's face while out walking. Fight or flight. The sympathetic nervous is stimulated and responds with an outpouring of *adrenaline* (epinephrine in the US) from the suprarenal (adrenal) medulla. This causes pupillary dilation, increased heart rate (tachycardia) sweating, shaking and raising of hair. There may be loose bowels and fainting – a vaso-vagal attack. .

Anxiety is the emotional response to a more remote danger or threat. When anxiety appears to be irrational to others, it is described as a *phobia*. Many phobias are described – *acrophobia*, fear of heights for instance, in fact 107 specific phobias have been described. (**W.B. Terhune**, 1949, who studied 86 patients).

1. *Agarophobia*. This is derived from the Greek αγορα meaning a market place rather than the Latin *agger* meaning a field. It was first described by the German Dr **C. Westphal** in 1872. People are not fearful of open spaces but they are of crowded places. The classic case is that of the housebound housewife, who is terrified of going out. Sometimes she finds comfort in being accompanied by a child or even a dog, but it is an extremely disabling condition leading to much family tension. Sufferers may go undiagnosed and therefore untreated for years as they are unable to attend a doctors' surgery. They are considerably helped by 'antidepressants' or sedatives and psychotherapy. One can see its origin in antiquity when 'going out' unaccompanied was extremely dangerous. In fact there are places in

the world today where going out unaccompanied is dangerous. Some places indeed where it is dangerous to go out without an armed guard. So perhaps they are not so irrational after all.

2. *Dysmorhophobia.* A portmanteau word to describe people who don't like the shape they are, their appearance, or even their sexual apparatus. They offer a good living to those who are able to effect the desired transformation. The long term effects of such transformations remains uncertain. One is reminded of 'Kristol's Law' which states – 'Frustration may be unpleasant but your troubles only really start when you get what you want.' The British Association of Aesthetic Plastic Surgeons reported that from 2002-2003 11,000 cosmetic procedures were performed, of which 20% were breast enlargement. 8% were performed on men, the nature of which was not stated.

3. *Cancerphobia* Perhaps the saddest of all phobias. Sufferers are ripe for exploitation by every quack and charlatan, who are anxious to 'diagnose' the disease with a black box with knobs and dials, and to provide a 'cure' – a course of 'treatment' at considerable expense. The trouble is that one cannot prove a negative – one cannot state with absolute certainty that a patient has not got cancer. One can do all the tests under the sun – all negative – but still it is possible that the tests are not sensitive enough. Another huge problem is that there are always false positives – the test proves positive but the patient has not got cancer – and false negatives – the test is negative but the patient has got cancer. Only time will tell. And therein lies the problem. Newspapers and magazines latch on to this and increase their circulation by alarming patients with 'if only' horror stories. It is also a good source for litigation lawyers to live in the style to which they have become accustomed.

Sir William Osler, one time Professor of Physic at Oxford University said – 'Cancer is a word that should always be in a doctor's mind but never on his lips.' Times have changed and patients are deemed to have a right to all information, uncertain as it may be. Which brings us to the latest phobic anxiety state which might be called *'litigophobia,'* the fear of all professionals of being sued, which leads to much unnecessary investigation and consequent anxiety, both to the doctor and to the patient, and much expense.

4. Children sometimes suffer from phobic anxiety states. In decreasing order of dread, 2-6 year olds listed dogs, doctors, darkness, deep water and

storms. 6-12 year olds listed supernatural events (ghosts, witches, corpses, mysterious events), being alone or lost, attack by animals, and bodily injury. Often their mothers suffered similarly so there may well be a familial aetiology.

5. Recently, another phobic anxiety state has been identified – *homophobia*. This, presumably, means a morbid dread of homosexuals.

Post-traumatic Stress Disorder (PTSD)

Shell shock was a diagnosis coined during the first World War (1914-1918) to describe those afflicted with a variety of symptoms, such as paralysis, amnesia, blindness, disorientation, mutism, for which no organic or physical cause could be found, and occurring in soldiers who had been exposed to the most appalling traumas, constant deafening noise, seeing their comrades blown to pieces, etc., etc. Initially they were diagnosed as malingering, or 'LMF' – Lacking in Moral Fibre – and sometimes summarily shot at dawn, 'to encourage the others.' A well known British response. These symptoms could be described as 'hysterical' or, better 'dissociation' after Janet's notation. Other 'diagnoses' were invented, such as 'Disorderly action of the Heart' and Da.Costa's syndrome, concepts that are no longer held today.

By 1916 the term ceased to be respectable and by 1918 it's use was banned altogether, though it did not go away. Sometimes the symptoms could be abolished under hypnosis, though they tended to relapse. The troops suffered from 'hysteria', but the officers suffered from 'neurasthenia', which was somehow thought to be more respectable. Casualties were evacuated from the front line, back to England 'We can't be encumbered with lunatics in Army areas'.

Some were called 'shell-shock wounded' which entitled them to a wound stripe and a pension. Others were called 'shell-shock S' (for sickness) which meant they were suffering from nervous collapse. During the battle of the Somme (July-December 1916), there were 16,139 cases of shell-shock wounded alone. But, following French experience, making sure casualties stayed in the military area, with refusal to pay pensions, thus eliminating the factor of secondary gain – frequently present in cases of nervous collapse, the cases were treated near the front line rather than being evacuated to England. In 1917, the year of Passchendale, there were 7,048 cases of Shell-shock.

A BRIEF HISTORY OF PSYCHIATRY

Recent accounts suggest that both the British and the Germans had 200,000 psychiatric casualties during the war, but statistics are unavailable for the French.

The American experience was similar, in spite of the fact that they had 3 years experience of correcting other peoples mistakes, and psychological testing of the troops prior to enlistment, there were 69,394 neuropsychiatric casualties. In 1927, there were 68,727 ex service men in hospital, 45% of the total.

In the second World War (1939-1945), Hitler said that 'neurosis' was to be treated as a disciplinary not a medical problem, and as a consequence, 15,000 German soldiers were executed.

— • —

In 1980, PTSD was defined in the third edition of the Diagnostic and Statistical Manual of Mental Disorders (DSM 3) and the condition became manifest following the Vietnam War (1955-1975). It was found that immediate breakdown was low (5% as opposed to 23% in World War 2), there were a considerable number of soldiers who found long term readjustment to civilian life very difficult.

But war was not the only stress factor. Any traumatic event, such as rape, assault, road traffic accident, may leave long term disability in some susceptible individuals. Hence it is being increasingly diagnosed. The factor of secondary gain, that is to say compensation, may in fact tend to prolong the disability. But there is evidence that the condition does not clear up even when the claims are settled.

Treatment involves anti-depressants and cognitive therapy.

Schizophrenia. (The word is sometimes used, incorrectly, by journalists and others to mean 'uncertain' or 'in two minds'. The correct usage is as described below).

A disease principally of the age group 12 to 35. The term schizophrenia was introduced by the Swiss psychiatrist Eugen Bleuler about 1900.

In order to understand its psychopathology it is necessary to understand the mechanism of the brain, and for that a computer analogy is useful. If one assumes that consciousness is the interface between the physical (brain) and the nonphysical elements of the personality (mind) one can make the analogy of memory being the 'hard disc' of the computer, into which all experience, conscious and unconscious, is processed.

Consciousness is the 'Desk Top.' Attention is the sharp edge of consciousness The little arrow manipulated by the mouse is 'attention' . The 'click' of the mouse is the 'aha' factor, recognition and understanding and comprehension. In a word – meaning.

In schizophrenia this mechanism is totally disrupted. Nothing has meaning. The patient is truly alienated. This is psychosis. Thoughts cannot be organized, irrelevant sensations assume great significance. Boundaries are broken down and the world, and speech, become incoherent. There are feelings of reference and external control. Auditory hallucinations (pathognomonic of the condition) arise, which cannot be ignored or suppressed, and sometimes have to be acted out. The patient cannot concentrate enough to follow a swinging pendulum. Time congeals and thinking becomes blocked. The computer 'crashes'. It will accept no input, and there is no output. The brain is not working and the patient is unable to get on with his or her life. In such circumstances suicide is an ever-present risk.

Aetiology is uncertain, though there is an element of heredity (genetic). If one identical twin has it there is said to be a 50% chance of the other developing it. A series of 47 children born to schizophrenic mothers in hospital and brought up in foster homes was studied by **Heston**. A control series of 50 children was identified, and they were followed up for 36 years. There was a 5% incidence of schizophrenia in the first group. None in the control group. Although faulty upbringing has been alleged to be a factor, there is little evidence for this.

There may be dopamine imbalance in the basal ganglia. There may be failure of myelination of nerves of the pre-frontal cortex at puberty.

The prognosis is uncertain; patients wander about, from town to town, often from one country to another. It is extraordinarily difficult to 'follow-up' out-patients. In the days of the large psychiatric hospitals many schizophrenics may have recovered but discharge became impossible as there was nowhere for patients to go, their 'domain' had gone. They were then diagnosed as suffering from 'institutional neurosis.' If they had financial resources they could be released into better care and accommodation, others were stuck. Then, in the 1960s, the large psychiatric hospitals were closed down, largely due to the introduction of *chlorpromazine* (*largactil*) and long-term *depixol* which could be injected and did not therefore require the patient's cooperation, and their analogues. They were replaced by 'care in the community' which unfortunately often turned out to be neglect, owing to inadequate resources, and the unfortunate sufferers ended up either as drug addicts or in jail, or perhaps both, not a happy ending.

Thus the prognosis remains uncertain. It is said that 50% recover, 25% have relapses, and a further 25% remain in need of care. But this excludes those who die from suicide, not a small number. Provided the patient has emotional support (somebody loves him or her), the prognosis is better. There is some evidence that schizophrenics survive better in families with low degrees of expressed emotion rather than those with high degrees of expressed emotion.

Treatment includes both drugs and psychotherapy and omega 3 EPA – a polyunsaturated fatty acid.

A medication called *Kirunal* has been advocated as a treatment for schizophrenia. This is a derivative of fish oil and in a dose of 8 grams a day contains about 2 grams of EPA (eicosipentanoic acid). The theory is that this replaces brain lipoids that may be deficient in schizophrenia. (See Appendix 1) At least it should not have too many undesirable side effects.

There are now many 'anti-psychotic' drugs on the market which have revolutionized the prognosis. But it is equally important to involve therapists to help patients to regain their 'domain' (see Chapter 4 Psychopharmacy – phenothiazines) The phrase *schizo-affective* disorder is used to describe patients who become depressed owing to the dysfunction of their brain.

Suicide

To Be, or Not to Be, – That is the Question.'
Whether 'tis nobler in the mind to suffer
The slings and arrows of outrageous fortune,
Or to take arms against a sea of troubles,
And by opposing end them?
Hamlet. Act III scene 1. Shakespeare.

Man is the only animal (except possibly lemmings,) that has the capability of self destruction.

Suicide is not a diagnosis; it is a verdict, reached by a Coroner (in Scotland, a Sheriff) following an inquest into a death in circumstances in which a doctor is unable to give a certificate as to the cause of death. Doctors are required by law to give a certificate of death in patients whom he has been attending, at least for the preceding fortnight.

Just as there are three factors in murder – opportunity, method and motive, so there are three factors in suicide – 1. Social isolation. 2. An unshakeable conviction of worthlessness, and 3. A 'trigger' factor, an event that seems quite trivial, to others, that precipitates the act. It is not uncommon in jail, all three factors above acting together.

The Catholic Church considers suicide a 'sin' (the actual sin is despair) punishable by eternal damnation, which may have been somewhat of a deterrent. In England for many years it was considered a crime, and the unfortunate overdosers were accompanied by police. Fortunately this law was repealed in the 1960s.

There are said to be about 7-8000 suicides a year in England and Wales, though figures for this are somewhat circumspect as coroners are sometimes reluctant to bring in this verdict, perhaps for religious reasons or to spare the relative's feelings and ensure benefit from insurance policies. They then bring in verdicts of accidental death, or an open verdict, when there is insufficient evidence of intent. Sometimes oxygen deprivation by suffocation, in an attempt to improve sexual satisfaction, goes tragically wrong.

There are many methods of suicide, hanging , jumping from a height, shooting, drowning, poisoning, but the most cruel is 'one under' – throwing oneself under the wheels of a train – of which there are about 5-600 a year in the UK. The unfortunate driver of the train is so shocked by the event that he never drives another train. The saddist and most tragic is the 12 year old boy who hangs himself from a lavatory cistern with a bath towel. Suicide in this age group is uncommon, but there has been an alarming rise in the suicide rate of males between the ages of 20-24 in the past few years.

In recent years suicide has become political. The worst to date (2004) was on 11 September 2001 (9.11.in US notation) when suicide bombers crashed their planes into the Twin Towers, the headquarters of the World Trade Organisation in New York City, with the deaths of 3,500 people. The

WTO was perceived to be an organisation, by its system of tariffs, quotas and subsidies, especially the dumping of surplus subsidised produce (sugar in the case of France, cereal grains in the case of the USA) to be devoted to ensuring that the rich get richer and the poor get poorer, and the poor get increasingly resentful, and demand change.

By a process of indoctrination, similar to Pavlov's dogs, groups of people can be induced to believe almost anything, no matter how irrational. This was done in China during the dictatorship of Mao Tse Tung, by 'cadres' in which youths were indoctrinated to overthrow the established society, the Cultural Revolution and the 'Great Leap Forward' in the 1960s, with immense suffering, the execution of over 100,000 people and a 20 year setback to the general economy.

Madrasas (religious schools) have been used to indoctrinate Muslim youths with similar fanaticism. In Japan in World War II the kamakasi dive-bomber pilots were conditioned to kill themselves.

In 2003, 34000 Japanese (15-25 age group) committed suicide mostly by gassing in cars, after meeting in internet 'chat rooms', an increase of 7% on the previous year – cybersuicide or perhaps cybercide. (Autocide is deliberately crashing one's car). One technique is to use a charcoal burner with barbecue brickettes to generate carbon monoxide in a closed space. There is a view that some SSRI anti-depressants, turn a retarded depression into an agitated one, thereby increasing the risk of suicide. It would be interesting to know how many of the Japanese were on this type of anti-depressant.

Death before Dishonour is the motive for some suicides, especially military ones. Captain Hans Langdorff, commander of the German battleship Graf Spee, scuttled his ship when it was trapped in the estuary of the River Plate by the British destroyers Ajax, Achilles and Exeter, in World War II, thereby saving many sailors' lives, rather than fight a battle which he was doomed to lose. He hated Hitler and all he stood for. On December 20th, 1939, he wrapped the flag of the Imperial German Navy around him and shot himself in the German Embassy in Montevideo. *Hara-kiri* (disembowelling) is the Japanese method suicide of those suffering 'loss of face'.

In 1953 the Samaritans organization was set up by Rev. Chad Varah. This is a telephone service by which those in distress can be heard by trained counsellors.

Attempted suicide – self harming

It is a sad reflection on economically advanced societies that, in 2003, 170,000 cases of self harm, mainly overdoses and cutting, were seen in NHS Hospital Casualty departments. Overdosers commonly take over-the-counter drugs such as aspirin or paracetamol. The latter can cause liver failure so must be treated seriously. The commonest prescription drug to cause death is co-proxamol. (800 per year) These are regarded as 'cries for help' but too often help is offered but refused. There may be an underlying depressive state and it may be a response to a sense of loss following a breakdown in relationships. There can be an element of attention seeking but there is also often an underlying personality disorder due to unresolved childhood trauma. Ideally a course of psychotherapy (cognitive behaviour therapy) may help but for economic and other reasons this is seldom available. As with suicide, victims have loss of self esteem and a perceived social isolation – 'nobody loves me', and sadly they don't even like themselves. Bulimia and anorexia nervosa come into the self-harming category. Unfortunately they do sometimes succeed in their attempts so they must be taken seriously.

Assisted suicide – (Sometimes incorrectly called *euthanasia*)
Etymologically, euthanasia means 'a well death'. Devoutly to be wished by all – the absence of pain and suffering. But somebody has to administer the fatal dose if one is unable to do it oneself. Ideally therefore, the patient should be able to terminate his or her existence so that nobody else can be blamed. If a 'third party' is involved, motivation may be involved. Whose suffering is being terminated, the patient's or the 'carer's'? Then the law steps in and further complicates the issue. Mostly the difficulty in defining circumstances legally is so great that no law would be considered appropriate in all circumstances. It is perhaps best left to the judgement of the next of kin and the attending physician. There seems little point in preserving a body when the soul has long departed. Hopefully the law will soon reflect this by refraining to make any laws. In order that justice is seen to be done, and to avoid irregularities, assisted suicide cases must be referred to the coroner, who will hear the evidence, consider the circumstances and pronounce a verdict of assisted suicide.

A report in the BMJ of 7.5.05 said that the Dutch had approved assisted suicide in a case of Alzheimer's disease. The Netherlands' assessment committee system consists of 5 regional committees to check that the requirements have been correctly followed. The committees consist of doctors, lawyers and ethicists to whom requests for assisted suicide must report. Only 4 out of 1886 cases reported in 2004 failed to meet the legal requirements, and these were reported to the Public Prosecutions service. .

CHAPTER FOUR
PSYCHOTHERAPY

I. PSYCHOTHERAPY

Is 'Training' nothing more than indoctrination and a way of becoming a 'professional' and achieving status? asked **Jeffrey Masson**. He says that he spent 8 years in psychoanalytic training and feels, in retrospect, that he could have learned the basic ideas in 8 hours of concentrated reading.

Intense professional group loyalty occurs in 'training' and anyone who doubts its validity or criticises it is 'excommunicated'. A therapist who disapproves of ECT must keep his misgivings to himself or he will be ostracised and his life made so difficult that he quits and may find difficulty in finding another job. Group loyalty is an instinctive phenomenon, deeply buried in our ancestry, when it was crucial for the survival of the tribe. It is easy to see how one can be sucked into the most appalling error, corruption and cruelty.

From 1930 to 1950 psychoanalysis predominated as 'treatment' for practically anything. Since psychotherapists had to be medically qualified, the 'medical model' of 'diagnosis' and 'treatment' was deemed appropriate…. 'I am the 'Doctor.' I am clever and powerful'. 'You are the 'patient' You are weak and ignorant'. I can get you 'better'.

Jung defined the purpose of psychoanalysis as 'to educate people to lead more fulfilling lives'.

In recent years psychotherapy is falling into disrepute owing to its damaging effect on family relationships.

The Physician or Therapist can hear the Confession, but cannot pronounce the Absolution. This can only be done by the Priest. A prescription is not enough.

Psychotherapy may have an element of brain washing. **William Sargant** describes the comments of a patient who had undergone Freudian analysis:- 'For the first few months I was able to feel nothing but increasing anxiety, humiliation and guilt. Nothing about my past life seemed satisfactory any more. When I got into a completely hopeless state he (Freud) then seemed to start to restore my confidence in myself, and to piece everything together in a new setting.' Analysis is often considered complete only when the therapist's points of view have been thoroughly absorbed and resistance (negative transference) to the therapist's interpretations of past events has broken down.

Many 'therapies' have been described, and been popular for a while. This may be more a reflection of the economic state of the society in that 'patients' can afford the fees of the therapists. Thus there has been

1. Transactional Analysis. (Berne – 1961)
2. Gestalt therapy (Perls et al 1951)
3. Primal therapy (Janov 1970)
4. Reality therapy (Glasser 1965)

At the moment (2004), Cognitive Behaviour Therapy has the high ground. – see below:

PSYCHOANALYSIS IN VARIOUS COUNTRIES

	1931	1954
Austria	57	12
Belgium	-	11
France	32	46
Germany	50	15
Italy	-	22
Netherlands	21	60
Switzerland	28	44
Israel	-	22
Britain	54	147
USA	69+29 = 98	2754
Hungary	22	-
Argentina	-	49
Brazil	-	36
Spain	0	0
India	26	not known

A BRIEF HISTORY OF PSYCHIATRY

An Analysis of the Analysts

i. Dr Sigmund Freud

It is generally accepted that Dr Sigmund Freud (1856-1939) was the father of psycho-analysis, a form of 'treatment' somewhat discredited but still popular amongst certain people.

In order to understand a person's ideas and motivation it is necessary to examine their background. Sigmund Freud was the son of Jacob, a Jewish wool merchant living in Freiburg, Moravia, a German speaking province, born on 6th of May, 1856. He was 40 when Sigmund was born and was described as 'remote'. His mother Amalie (Nathansohn) was 20 and was Jacob's 3rd wife. She was a warmer personality. A sister Anna was born in 1858. From Jacob's earlier marriage, Sigmund had 2 older half-brothers. Sigmund was the first born. The family employed a nursemaid who was a Catholic and dragged him to Church in his infancy. His half brother Philip had her arrested and sent to jail on a charge of theft and little Siggy was devastated. Jacob abandoned Hasadic principles and observed only the Purim and Passover.

The family moved to Vienna in 1859 and Sigmund studied medicine. He became interested in the pharmacology of cocaine. A friend had noticed that the tip of his tongue became numb when touched with cocaine, and he introduced its use as a local anaesthetic. Unfortunately, some people have an idiosyncratic response to cocaine, develop anaphlylaxis and occasionally, die. So cocaine is no longer used as an anaesthetic and has been superseded by derivatives such as procaine, lignocaine and amethocaine. This was probably Freud's most important contribution to Medicine. Unfortunately he developed a taste for this particular medicine. He was also a compulsive smoker, which could well have contributed, at the age of 67, to the occurrence of a cancerous condition of his palate, for which he had 30 operations. Even when told of the connection, he was unable to stop.

From October 1885 until February 1886 he went to work in the Salpetrière Clinic in Paris under Jean-Marie Charcot, who was treating patients who suffered from conversion hysteria (blindness, paralysis etc.) with hypnosis (belief + expectation + misdirected attention). Such conditions, where an underlying anxiety causes ideas to become symptoms (somatisation), are seldom seen in developed countries today. He learnt from Charcot that disability was due to faulty ideas, which could be altered by hypnosis. In 1886 he started medical practice in Vienna. His only experience of severe mental illness was a 3-week locum at the at Oberdöbling, a small private hospital. He saw cases of paranoia and dementia praecox (schizophrenia) but deemed them unsuitable for psycho-analysis.

In 1886 he married Martha Bernays who was a sustaining influence in his life and career, and they had 6 children. This led to the abandonment of his career in research, as he had to earn a living.

A patient, Bertha Pappenheim, (Annie O) was referred to him suffering from hysterical symptoms (shortness of breath). Instead of using hypnosis, Freud treated her by 'talking out' her symptoms, 'abreaction' – the discharge of pent-up emotional blockage. This is the underlying basis of psychoanalysis, and the source of the blockage was alleged to be sexual frustration. (This notion was of course very popular with youth at the time and may well have led to the reduction of Victorian prudery and contributed to Freud's popularity.) He wrote 24 volumes, and published reports of 133 cases, but only 6 extended accounts. He recognized that adolescents pushed into treatment by their parents seldom did well. He was good with obsessionals, as he was one himself. He had a high regard for himself and his ideas, and would not take 'no' for an answer. *'He never presented any data in statistical or case study form, that could have demonstrated that his treatment was of benefit to a significant number of the patients he himself saw.*(Fisher & Greenberg et al – The scientific credibility of Freud's theories and therapy – (New York 1977)

But therapy does help people to come to terms with difficulties such as transvestism and homosexuality, without attempting to 'cure' them, by accepting them for what they are – positive transference.

Freud insisted that that sexual energy (Libido) was the primary driving force in relationships, a notion that is no longer held, and led to the split, after many years of friendship, with Jung. He later realized that many of his patient's notions and beliefs had in fact been implanted in them by himself during his analytic sessions.

Freud, in the early stages of his work, claimed that almost all hysterical women coming to him for treatment gave him a history of sexual interference, often of a perverted kind, and of incest, by their fathers. This was almost certainly due to his being so interested in this particular line of enquiry that he unknowingly implanted the ideas in the patient's minds, and then got them given back to him; the emotional stresses of the treatment making him and his patients reciprocally suggestive.

Up to the spring of 1897 Freud still held firmly to his conviction of the reality of these childhood traumas. Then, quite suddenly, it dawned on him the awful truth that most of these seductions had never occurred. The result of this was total bewilderment. In the 1990s False Memory Syndrome had a vogue in the USA. Children under therapy accused their fathers of abusing them, the cause of their trouble. This caused many appalling miscarriages of justice as families were torn apart, fathers often jailed, the families ruined.

Dr John Bowlby thought that secure attachment came first, sex afterwards.

Many patients enjoy psycho-analysis. The friendly uncritical acceptance, a dedicated listener, never angry, never rejecting, so that termination of treatment can be difficult. Patients find that it boosts their self-esteem and they can make more fulfilling relationships.

Psycho-analysis became a belief system, though Freud insisted that it was a 'science' that he had 'discovered', yet it is far from scientific, incapable of refutation and cannot be used for prediction. Criticism was heresy, punished by exclusion, just as heresy was punished by the Catholic Church with excommunication.

Critics such as Jung, Adler, Steckel and others were labelled 'neurotic, or 'psychotic' and highly intemperate language was used. Objectivity had vanished.

Freud was an alpha-dominant, charismatic male, unable to tolerate dissension, seized with total conviction of the correctness of his ideas, disregarding those who are perplexed by the uncertainties of this life. In 1928 his name was put forward to the Nobel Prize committee. Einstein among others refused to support it. He was rejected on the grounds that he was 'a fraud and a menace'.The basis of psycho-analysis is as follows:

1. Free association.
2. Interpretation of dreams.
3. Evaluation of transference and counter-transference.
4. The therapist must sit out of sight of the patient, who reclines on a couch.

(Freud did not like being stared at.)
5. Freud encouraged emotional detachment.
6. The therapist must have been psycho-analysed. (This was Jung's suggestion)
7. The patient must not be patronized by handing out unsolicited advice.
8 One hour of each working day is allotted.
9. Payment is to be made at the end of the session, whether the patient attends or not. (To encourage attendance.)

Selection of patients is as follows.:

1. Reasonable degree of education and reliable character. No psychotics, anorexics or depressives. (Manics do not apply)
2. A trial period of 1-2 weeks to assess suitability.
3. Age limit of 50 or nearabouts, as older people had too much material and were considered ineducable. Adolescents were considered more amenable. Freud denied the influence of suggestion, but clearly this was a important factor.
4. Would not take on relatives or friends unless one is prepared to sacrifice that friendship (though for 2 years Freud did psycho-analyse his daughter Anna, the only one of his children to become a psycho-analyst.)
5. Patient must have an unconditional positive attitude.

ii. Dr Carl Gustav Jung (1875- 1961)

His father Paul was a Protestant Pastor who had a living at Kiswil near Basel, Switzerland. His mother was Emilie Preiswerk, the daughter of a Pastor. Their first 3 children died soon after birth and Emilie had become despondent. Carl was their fourth child, a 'robust large boned blond boy, the image of his father'. When he was 6 months old, the family moved to a better parish at Laufen. But Emilie remained withdrawn, probably suffering from puerperal depression, and spent most of her time in her room and Carl was looked after by a maid. The marriage was not happy at the time, and Paul suffered from frequent rages. His mother began seeing ghosts and apparitions and went to stay at a rest home near Basel and Carl went to stay with his Aunt Gusteli. He spent much of his time alone. He had a recurrent dream of a 'phallus' and his mother saying ' Yes, just look at him, that is the man eater.'

It is possible that this refers to a time when he was in the company of a Jesuit priest who had exposed himself to the little boy. Naturally, such horrifying memories are suppressed, as the child is told never to reveal what happened, upon pain of being cast into hell. When he was 6 he went to the village school and excelled in everything except mathematics. When he was 9 Emilie gave birth to a sister, Johanna Gertrud, called Trudi in 1884.and young Carl was somewhat embarrassed by this display of carnality, as if his mother had done something that he was not supposed to know about.

At the age of 11 he matriculated to the Humanistisches Gymnasium in Basel, where all the best families sent their children and with his knowledge of Latin and the Bible, was the star pupil. He had to walk several miles to school each day and was ill clothed owing to his father's poverty. But he was avid for knowledge.

His father was appointed pastor/counsellor to the Basel psychiatric Clinic the Freidmatt, the University's mental hospital/asylum, which he greatly enjoyed, and his clinical duties took preference over his religious ones. Just before the end of his first year at school, Carl was pushed over and struck his head sharply on the ground, rendering him semi-conscious. He had to be carried home. From then on he was subject to fainting attacks, so much so that he had to be withdrawn from school. His father became very anxious about his welfare, and Carl overheard him say to a friend how worried he was that his son would never be able to earn a living. This hit Carl like a thunderclap and he set about returning to his studies with a vengeance, even though he felt faint at times, he managed to overcome this and returned to school.

When he was 15, he had to consider his career prospects. Both father and son entertained 'religious doubts' and it felt that a career in the church was not possible, though he had many relatives on his mothers' side who were pastors. However his grandfather Carl Gustav Jung I was a prominent and respected doctor in Basel society and this probably lent weight to his decision to become a doctor. His father had to petition local officials for the fees, provided he maintained his grades. Unfortunately Paul became seriously ill and died at the age of 54, probably of cancer of the pancreas.

Carl Gustav Jung II enrolled at the faculty of Natural Sciences at the University of Basel, and from 1885-1887 was happy following the set programme, basic science, anatomy, physiology, nutrition. But following the death of his father, no money was coming in to support his mother and sister and it was suggested he abandoned his medical studies and get a job. Carl was furious at this, and went to his uncle Ernst Jung for a loan, which was agreed. Carl did not like touching bodies, particularly dead ones, which precluded his ability to become a surgeon, so it seemed appropriate to specialize in psychiatry where a course had just been started in 1888 and which he joined in 1898. In 1900 he studied under **Prof. Ludwig Wille** who had founded the St Urban Cantonal Mental Asylum, the city's lunatic asylum. Wille believed that most psychoses had physical causes. Carl's mother Emilie had what might have been a dual personality. One was a placid housewife and mother, the other had visions and dabbled in the occult, 'psychic phenomena', and Carl was to inherit this curiosity and held séances.

His cousin Helene at the age of 14 was considered 'sensitive' and went into trances and made predictions, which often turned out to be accurate, and conducted exorcisms'. In 1895 Carl studied experiments in table tilting. The participants became increasingly frightened and disorientated by these phenomena and the séances finished in 1899 when Helly Preiswerk's mother Celestine sent her to Paris, where she became a talented seamstress and dress designer, eventually overseeing a salon employing 23 people.

Carl qualified as a doctor in 1900 and for his Doctoral Dissertation he wrote 'On the Psychology and Pathology of so-called Occult Phenomena.' submitting it to the University of Zurich rather than Basel as he wished to work under Dr Eugen Bleuler at the Burghölzli Mental Hospital. He applied and got the job as he was the only applicant – Bleuler had a notorious reputation for overworking his assistants.

Bleuler (1857-1939) believed in establishing rapport with patients by listening to them and getting them involved in all activities of the Asylum. He was the first member of his family to be educated beyond elementary school. His sister had catatonic schizophrenia. Earlier directors had regarded the Hospital as a warehouse where patients languished while the directors conducted research in order to gain an international reputation for them, and by extension, the Hospital. He had studied under **Auguste Forel,** an earlier director of the Burghölzli , who had great success with treatment of alcoholism. For the first 6 months Jung lived like a hermit, never leaving the Hospital grounds, and became confident in managing his share of the 400 patients in the Hospital.

Jung, together with **Franz Riklin**, elaborated the word-association tests that had been suggested by **Francis Galton**, refined by Wilhelm Wundt and used by Freud. They presented the patient with a list of 100 words and instructed them to respond with the first word that came to mind. Their refinement was to measure the degree of distress by the amount of time that it took to respond. Words such as 'marriage' and 'mother' provided striking insights into the subjects. They coined the term '*complex*' for a 'personal matter that was always a collection of various ideas held together by an emotional tone common to all'. He developed a 'psychogalvanometer' to add a touch of 'science', to his experiments. His word association tests came to the attention of the law courts and Jung was called to give evidence, thereby increasing his fame, especially in America.

In 1902, disenchanted with his job at the Burghölzli, he requested leave from Bleuler, and went to Paris to study the work of **Alfred Binet** (children's intelligence) and **Pierre Janet** (dissociation). He learnt English. Before going, he had to serve his yearly duty in the Swiss army. He was also secretly engaged to be married to Emma Rauschenbach, an intelligent and beautiful daughter of a wealthy industrialist. He married in 1903. He had earlier been described as 'somewhat timid with women' and his relationship with men was also probably coloured by an experience in childhood, which he described in old age. He claimed he was the victim of a sexual assault by an unknown person, but may have been a Jesuit priest who was a friend of his father, and he had a recurrent dream of what was probably a phallus.

He returned to the Burghölzli as a locum and and adjunct lecturer at Zurich University. His wife helped him in his studies in 'association'. His daughter Agathe Regina was born in December 1904.

Whereas Freud's patients came from a higher social strata, those who could afford his fees, Jung's were from the lower social order. His lectures were increasingly popular and well attended, particularly by the *Pelzmäntel*, the society fur-coat ladies, who sat in the front, while the students had to sit in the back. He began to neglect his duties at the Burghölzli to the annoyance of Bleuler, as other doctors had to do his work.

On Sept 15th, 1905, Jung wrote to Freud concerning a patient, Sabina Spielrein who was a 19 year old Russian girl who had come to Zurich as a medical student but had had several attacks of 'hysteria' and was admitted to the Burghölzli. She could not eat in company because of an irrational fear of defaecation, she could not look at people directly, she was prone to violent outbursts, and stuck out her tongue at people. For the next 7 years, until she qualified in 1911, her life was entwined with Jung, amidst much speculation, and to Emma's distress. She was the eldest of five children. Victims of an arranged marriage, her father was moody, prone to rages, threatening suicide when crossed, and her mother was described as 'exceedingly vain' and compensated by shopping for clothes and jewellery.

She was very intelligent, fluent in Russian, Polish, French and German by the age of 7, later adding English. Between the ages of 4 and 7, she was repeatedly beaten on the buttocks by her father in one of his rages, and became sexually aroused during this. In addition, her mother totally forbad her any information about reproductive physiology, and used her influence in the science curriculum at the Gymnasium to have all reference to reproduction to be omitted from the course. When informed by Jung that Sabina's problems had a sexual basis she was horrified.

She was refused admission by the Heller Clinic and so on August 17th, 1904, went to the public asylum the Burghölzli.

Because of her exceedingly difficult behaviour, pranks on the staff and tantrums, , Bleuler insisted on the payment of the highest fees, as the family 'seemed' very wealthy, 10 francs per day plus supplements. Her behaviour improved when she was allowed to take part in the hospital activities, particularly when Jung was doing his free association tests. A 'transference' situation developed tantamount to hero worship. By February 1906, she was sufficiently stable to be allowed to enrol at Zurich University.

Jung wrote to Freud 'During the treatment she had the misfortune to fall in love with me. Now she always raves ostentatiously to her mother about her love, and takes a secret spiteful joy in her mother's discomfort, and her mother wants someone else to treat her.' (Why do children play games with their parents? Perhaps they only grow up when their parents are dead) But Jung continued to 'treat' her – 'morally obliged' lest she relapsed. When Jung was psychoanalysed by his colleague at the Burghölzli. **Ludwig Binswanger**, he became extremely agitated at the 'sch' sound, presumably referring to Sabina Spielrien, and had to be told to calm down for a spell.

But Sabina was 'wild and outgoing', a 'force of nature, one to be reckoned with,' unlike Emma, who was deferential and shyly retiring, given to domestic duties, and pregnant. She gave birth to Anna Margareta (Gret) on February 8th, 1906.

Thus Jung had an opportunity to meet Freud for the first time, and Jung and Emma went to Vienna on March 3rd, 1907 and had lunch with the Freud family. Freud and Jung got on well and talked well into the night on their first meeting. But Jung's final impression of their first meeting was 'I could not make him out.'

In September, Jung was instrumental in setting up a meeting to propose the establishment of a Swiss Society for Freudian research, with 12 doctors.

After considerable arguments Jung managed to get a meeting organised on April 27th, 1908 in the Hotel Bristol, Salzburg. 42 people listened to 9 papers, but there was no chairman, agenda, no committee. But it was decided to set up a Journal, the *Jahrbuch fur psychoanalytisch und psychopathologisch Forschungen*, directed by Bleuler and Freud, edited by Jung. Subsequently this kept Jung busy for the next few months, but there was considerable rivalry between the various 'schools'.

During 1908 Jung became involved in the case of Dr Otto Gross, a brilliant doctor who had studied under Kraepelin in Munich, but suffered from manic -depressive disorder exacerbated by addiction to cocaine and opium. Jung was persuaded to take on his case, but in the end he was defeated, and after a year's treatment, 'escaped from the hospital by jumping over the wall,' never to be see by Jung again. Jung later told Freud that knowing him had been one of the two most bitter experiences of his psychoanalytic career, 'to none of my patients have I extended so much friendship, and from none have I reaped so much sorrow'.

On November 28th, 1908, Emma gave birth to a son, Franz Karl. But Jung was becoming increasingly involved with Sabina Spielrein. Jung wrote to Freud claiming that polygamy was the natural state of men and Freud apparently forgave him, and Jung 'painted himself as lily-white' to his wife Emma. But Emma refused to allow Sabina into her house.

On December 30th, Freud wrote to Jung saying he had had an invitation from **G.Stanley Hall**, President of Clark University, (USA) to deliver a series of lectures the following year. He rejected the invitation as the offered $400 was insufficient to offset his lost income. Jung replied that he should reconsider, as Kraepelin had been offered a 'modest tip' of 50,000 marks for one consultation in California recently.

On April 15th, 1909, Jung submitted his resignation from the Burghölzli, where he had been for the past 10 years, to Bleuler, to further his private scientific activities.

The same day as he resigned fate brought him a rich and powerful American patient, **Joseph Medill McCormick**, one of the heirs to a Chicago newspaper empire. He had suffered his second alcoholic break-down and was in Europe ostensibly on a business trip. He was admitted to the Burghölzli, under Jung, to Bleuler's intense annoyance. Alcoholism was Bleuler's special interest. Jung diagnosed Medill's trouble as stemming from the influence of his dominating mother, a 'power devil of the very first rate'. He must be removed from her influence. Jung sent a certificate to the Chicago Tribune stating that he was a hopeless alcoholic and permanently incapable of performing his duties. The paper was relieved to see him leave but his mother accepted this reluctantly. He returned to Chicago 'cured'.

This brought Jung a steady stream of Americans. (But in 1925 Medill committed suicide in his Washington Hotel room).

When President Hall informed that his fee had been increased to $750, Freud accepted, inviting **Ferenczi** to join him. Jung had also been invited and they sailed on the SS *George Washington* on August 21st, 1909.

'Legend has it that Freud and Jung stood on the deck together as the ship sailed into New York Harbour. Freud is said to have looked at the skyline of New York City and said 'If they only knew what we were bringing to them' Actually, he had put the matter more succinctly to Ferenczi many months earlier, when he worried that, as soon as the Americans discovered 'the sexual underpinnings of his psychology,' we could soon be up shit creek.'. He was right on both counts.'

Shortly after their arrival, Freud had an embarrassing attack of his 'neurosis., in that he urinated in his trousers, and Jung agreed to analyse him. (It is just possible that it was in fact due to his cocaine addiction). But this analysis did not progress very far as Freud whispered 'My dear boy, I cannot risk my authority.' (It was alleged that Freud had a sexual relationship with his sister-in-law Minna Bernhays'

After meeting the Clark's and having dinner with such notables as A.A. Michelson and Sir Ernest Rutherford, and the philosopher William James, they delivered their lectures and went touring , leaving the USA on September 22nd.

But Emma Jung was not happy. ' I find I have no friends, all the people who associate with us really only want to see Carl, except for a few . boring and uninteresting persons.' When she tried to discuss this with her husband, he told her to stop concentrating on him and the children. 'What am I to do' she wrote to Freud, 'all the women with whom she came into contact are in love with him'. (The diaries of these women gave strong hints at sexual encounters at their sessions). On his return from America, Carl agreed to psychoanalyse her. At least she had her husband's attention, and in fact gave her an insight into psychoanalysis and she became an analyst herself, and was able to understand and criticize his work. She also became fascinated by the legend of the Holy Grail.

Following his successful treatment of Medill McCormick, and his lectures at Clark, many wealthy Americans came over for treatment, and his practice vastly increased, and he thought of taking on a colleague , J.J. Honegger. However the latter's ideas and behaviour became increasingly erratic and he committed suicide on March 28th, 1911. He probably suffered from bipolar disorder, manic depressive illness.

In mid-1910, **Toni Anna Wolff** was brought to Jung by her mother, shortly after the death of her father. She was then 22, the eldest of 3 daughters. The family was affluent and cultured and Toni was 'sheltered, pampered, seeming much younger than her years.' She was glum and recalcitrant and depressed, grieving inconsolably. She had in common with Jung an interest in classical mythology and soon the depression lightened. In fact Emma welcomed Toni to help Carl with his psychoanalysis, and in a letter from Freud, told her she was 'a solver of riddles,' 'an uncannily accurate estimation of the role she would play for the rest of her life in the triangular relationship composed of herself, her husband, and Toni Wolff. '

Jung became increasingly busy with his psychoanalytic practice together with his editorship of various journals and Toni took an increasing part in his life. She was described then as 'elegantly prim, self-contained, and seemingly asexual, a poised articulate women, with carefully coiffed hair beneath a stylish cloche hat'. ' and was not perceived by Emma as a threat. Emma's primary emotion was that her husband had found in another woman the intellectual stimulation and friendship that she wanted to provide. (but was it love?) Previously Toni had been ' a skinny, twitchy, chain-smoker with fingernails bitten to the quick, messy hair and unkempt clothes. Emma was grateful for the library research that Toni did as she did not have time for it herself with four rumbustuous children.

But 1911 marked the beginning of the rift between Jung and Freud and the end of their collaboration. Jealousy probably had a lot to do with it apart from their fundamental disagreement about sex as the primary motivation of behaviour. In addition Freud thought that Jung was neglecting his duties as President of the Psychoanalytic Association, and Freud insisted on ultimate authority.

It was about this time that Jung began to formulate his theory of the collective unconscious.

Freud wrote to Jung that he intended to visit Ludwig Binswanger, arriving at Kreuzlingen, Lake Constance on May 24th, 1912. He did not invite Jung. This was the famous 'Kreuzlingen Gesture', and was the beginning of the end of the relationship between Jung and Freud.

On September 9th, Jung left for America, not to return until November. During this time, Emma wrote to Freud with warm and friendly comments, but Freud did not reply. Jung's nine lectures in America were attended by eighty eight psychiatrists, but Jung thought that 'they were only interested in how it is done, not in what it means.' By virtue of his treatment of Medill McCormick, he met President Theodore Roosevelt.

On his return, Jung met Freud in the Parkhotel Munich on December 14th. During a discussion about 'father complexes' Freud fainted which he attributed to 'repressed feelings' (but was it cocaine?). At any rate this marked the end of their friendship accompanied by insulting each other. On January 3rd, 1913, Jung wrote to Freud offering greetings for the New Year and hoping that psychoanalysis would continue to flourish, 'that my honourable intentions were perfectly clear and left the rest to you' .

Freud proposed total rupture, an end to anything personal between them. 'Take your freedom and spare me your supposed tokens of friendship'. Jung commented on their seven-year friendship – 'the rest is silence'.

Freud now did his best to exclude Jung from the rest of the psychoanalytic fraternity, causing Jung much distress, and he had what may have amounted to a nervous breakdown, a depressive episode, doing very little between the autumn of 1913 and the end of 1917. He suffered from terri-fying dreams, especially of decaying corpses -perhaps precognition of the Great War, and read no books during this period, since he was unable to concentrate, completely devastated, all pleasure in conscious work lost. He consoled himself with the thought – 'I have a Swiss diploma as a physi-cian, a wife and 5 children, and live at 228 Seestrasse, Küsnacht. Those were facts....I really do exist....(Nietzsche completely lost his sense of identity because he had nothing but the inner world). During this period Jung wrote two mystical semi-religious books, The Seven Sermons to the Dead' and 'The Red Book'., which helped to dispel his 'ghosts', perhaps guilt over his love of Toni Wolff. .

He spent his time playing with his children and talking to Toni Wolff, working towards his book 'Psychological Types', coining the words 'intro-vert' and 'extrovert.', published in 1921. Emma had her 5th baby, Emma Helene, on March 18th, 1914. Shortly after, Jung and Toni went for a hol-iday in Ravenna, and their relationship deepened, about which Jung felt guilty and rationalised his behaviour. His wife was not happy, given to out-bursts of seething rage, and with the break from Freud, she had no one to console her. Emma made few women friends because their wives were more interested in Jung's professional services than in inviting him and Emma to dinners where their husbands would have nothing to say to the 'quack mind doctor.' But she was a good hostess, serving dinners to many people, among whom was Albert Einstein, who ate his meals mostly in silence, immersed in thought.

Jung's profession set him and his family apart. 'All those foreigners. Those strange American zombies staying at the Hotel Sonne wandering the lakefront; that rich woman in the Hotel Baur au Lac; that club where they all practised strange rituals – well we stayed away from all that.' But by virtue of Emma's wealth, they were not entirely excluded. Jung's practice was prospering, patients coming from England and America as well as Zurich.

The Psychological Club of Zurich was founded, and paid for, by the introvert and intellectual Edith Rockefeller McCormick, the immensely wealthy daughter of John D. Rockefeller Sr, the Princess of Standard Oil. She was married to the extrovert and sporting non-intellectual Harold McCormick, the immensely wealthy Prince of International Harvester of Chicago. She met Jung by virtue of his involvement with Medill McCormick. The purchase of the grand house No. 1 Lowenstrasse was signed on January 26th, 1916, as a meeting place for 'analysed people'. There were 24 women and 16 men as founder members, additional members brought the total to 55. Jung was the official owner as he was Swiss, and Emma was chairwoman. Controversy reigned over its purpose and owing to expense, the house was sold and the club moved into cheaper premises later, on September 1919, and it later, in 1924, became what Edith had always intended, a place for the dissemination of the ideas of C.G.Jung.

The meetings were dominated by Jung in the centre, Emma on one flank, Toni on the other. The problem of 'rank' arose, amidst much animosity. But in spite of it all, Edith and Harold were divorced in 1921.

The publication of Psychological Types in 1921 marked a new confidence in Jung's life as his ideas became widespread and acknowledged, though not necessarily accepted. . His admirers called him 'the wisest man I have ever known' – 'the man who saved my life'. His detractors 'a perfect fool'.

But from 1920 onwards, with the end of the war, his practice flourished and his 'waiting list' became over a year. Many unhappy people stayed at the cheap Hotel Sonne, disconsolately wandering the streets of Zurich. The social collapse of the Edwardian era left many uncertainties and disillusionments.

In 1915 **James Joyce** came to Zurich, a refugee from Trieste, where he had been interned with his wife and 2 children. Always on the verge of penury, he came to the attention of Edith McCormick in 1918. She deemed him worthy of benefaction and settled, anonymously, an annual stipend of 12,000 Swiss francs to be deposited in a bank account on Joyce's name. He later discovered the source of his wealth and wrote her a letter of thanks, though he never met her. Joyce was a major curiosity in Zurich at the time, spending his time in cafes and restaurants, but in fact he was writing *Ulysses*. Also in Zurich was **Lenin**, 'scribbling in solitude in the Café Odeon', until the sealed train took him to St. Petersburg.

Joyce wrote ' A batch of people in Zurich persuaded themselves that I was going mad and endeavoured to get me to enter a sanatorium where a certain Dr Jung (The Swiss Tweedledum who is not to be confused with the Viennese Tweedledee, Dr Freud, amuses himself at the expense(in every sense of the word) of ladies and gentlemen who have troubles with bees in their bonnets'.

Mrs McCormick later cut off his stipend as she alleged 'he is extremely lazy and never finishes anything'. This was very galling to Joyce as he had spent 20,000 hours writing *Ulysses*.

In 1919 Jung was invited to England to lecture and he transferred his affection from America to England and dressed himself in Harris Tweeds and brown brogues and 'looked like a genial English cricketer', and he had many female admirers.

In late 1922 Jung bought a plot of land near the village of Bollingen and had a tower built on it, to be round with a cooking hearth in the middle. He stayed in it mostly alone, and in 1927 added more space and in 1931 added a second tower to accommodate his guests. The first tower was symbolically Emma's, the second, Toni's. But he was adamant that no indoor plumbing or electricity was to be included. He had a wall built around it to discourage sightseers. He began to carve stones. During the period 1919 to 1925, he was a frenetic traveller, going to England, France, Germany, Holland, twice to Africa, twice to America.

In 1925 Jung, together with George Beckwith, a wealthy Chicagoan, and Peter Baynes, embarked on a voyage to Africa, to Mount Elgon, Bugishu, Kenya, to study and get an insight into primitive African tribal customs. During the voyage to Mombasa, Jung met a lady, **Ruth Bailey**, out to chaperone her sister who was engaged to be married. They struck up a lasting friendship, and she was invited to join the expedition, to her intense relief in not having to enjoy colonial life in Nairobi. She became the organiser of the expedition, a calming influence, keeping the men from falling out. She wrote – ' CG (as she always called him) did not make me adore him, like all those women at home did. I never did that, and that is where the success lay in the end. That is why my relationship with him lasted so long.'

Jung wrote about the trip 'For me, the trip was a drama. One could say the drama of the birth of light, because that was most intimately linked to me, to my psychology. It was extremely enlightening to me, but on the other hand, I felt completely incapable of putting it into words. It wouldn't mean anything to other people anyway! I also wouldn't have been able to bear that people might have thought that I had made up the fact that the Elgonyi had this religion that God was the moment. No one knows that after all, and now it is already lost anyway.' He realised afterwards that he had undertaken the African journey, not so much for scientific study, but because the atmosphere had become too highly charged at home.

Jung was 50 in 1925. He devoted the rest of his life toward defining the collective unconscious, primarily through his study of alchemy. (He could recite all 64 hexameters of the I Ching from memory.) He became Professor Jung. He held weekly seminars, in English, for the next 14 years. There were more English and American attenders than German or Swiss, held at the Psychological Cub in Gemeindestrasse, still its home today. At the time he was charging 50 francs an hour for his therapy, and his clients were mostly female.

The physicist **W.E.Pauli** (of the Exclusion Principle) came to Jung in 1931, on account of terrifying dreams. Jung at first refused to see him, referring him to Erna Rosenbaum, an associate of Jung, but in 1932 he met Jung and formed a friendship that lasted 26 years.

In 1931 **F.Scott Fitzgerald** was skiing in Lausanne while his wife **Zelda** was in the Nyon sanatorium under Auguste Forel. Forel was keen for Zelda to go the Burghölzli under Bleuler, or to be under Jung. Fitzgerald settled for the former, as he felt Jung dealt only with neurosis, and Zelda should be confined. He complained that both Bleuler and Jung charged $500 for an initial consultation.

In 1933 Joyce's daughter Lucia was behaving very erratically and Joyce took her to be examined by **Dr Hans Meier**, staff physician at the Burghölzli, who sent her to Forel at Prangins who diagnosed schizophrenia. Joyce then discharged her and went to Paris. But after a year they could not cope, and returned her to Forel. She set fire to her room and was returned to the Burghölzli. She stayed one week and her father removed her to a private clinic, the Brunner at Küsnacht. Jung then became the 20th psychiatrist to supervise Lucia's treatment. Jung was no more successful then any other and deputed his colleague Cary Baynes to supervise her. She had some success with craft therapy but Joyce was unwilling to accept the situation. Jung was 'perplexed' by Joyce's writing and their relationship was somewhat cool. He wrote 'In any other time of the past Joyce's work would never have reached the printer, but in our blessed XX Century it is a message, though not yet understood.'. Joyce felt that if Jung could not understand *Ulysses*, he could not understand his daughter.

In January 1935 Joyce took Lucia back to Paris, where she continued her downward path. Ultimately Jung thought that the novel was 'a work of Anti-Christ.' Jung also had difficulty with the later paintings of Picasso.

On December 4th,1937 Jung set sail for India, with Fowler McCormick whom he had met earlier. They visited various cities and in Allahabad and Benares Jung received honorary degrees. But Jung got a severe attack of amoebic dysentery, which was to plague him for the next few years. He studied Buddhism. – 'The Buddha overcomes the world out of insight. Christ does not overcome out of insight, but as an event, for he is the victim.'

In 1928 Jung had become a charter member of a German organization called the International General Medical Society for Psychotherapy. A journal was started, which became the *Zentralblatt für Psychotherapie* with Dr Sommer, later Dr Ernst Kretschmer as editor., later President of the Society, with Jung as vice president. Kretschmer wrote 'There is something strange about psychopaths. In normal times we write expert evaluations on them; in times of political unrest, they rule us.'.When the Nazis came to power in 1933, all things Jewish were anathema, hence Freud's ideas were rejected, in fact his books were burnt. Freud escaped to England in 1939. But Jung's association with the German organisation brought his reputation into disrepute, though he claimed he was doing his best to help the Jewish psychotherapists.

During the war there was much privation in Switzerland with rationing, and in the early years there was fear that the Germans would invade, and the Jung family evacuated to the Bernese Oberland. Jung was telephoned to say that his name was on a Nazi *Schwarze List* – those named for arrest and incarceration or worse and he hastily joined his family. Basel and Zurich were bombed by the Allies in December 1940, specific industrial sites being targeted.

Owing to his German connections Jung was attached to the US intelligence – Agent 488, by **Allen W. Dulles**, special assistant to the ambassador to Berne, to assess the state of mind of the German leaders. During the later stages of the war, which the Germans were losing, one of Hitler's doctors asked Jung to go to Berchtesgarten to observe him on account of his increasingly erratic behaviour and his heavy drinking. The generals wanted a report to justify their desire to have him removed. Jung declined.

On February 11th, 1944, at the age of 69, he slipped while out walking and fractured his fibula. He was put to bed but suffered a pulmonary embolism 10 days later, and he lost consciousness and had various hallucinations in his delirium. 'I was on my way of taking leave from Earth' – he was grateful for these experiences and concentrated on enjoying them. He was very depressed after this and resented being called back 'from the horizon of the cosmos to the grey world.' Jung had a vision of the attending doctor's (Haemmerli)death – 'he was in his Ur gestalt, and when someone has reached this gestalt, it means they will soon die' On April 4th, 2 months after his fall, he was allowed to sit out. He never forgot the date because that was the day Dr Haemmerli was taken ill and died of septicaemia several days later. Jung hovered in a delirium for some weeks, with Emma always at his bedside. No bulletins were issued and for several months only the children were allowed to visit, to Toni Wolff's grief.

He was released form hospital at the end of June, so weak that he could not climb stairs, and Emma took total charge of the situation.

He slowly recovered and spent the next few years justifying his attachment to the Germans, but in November 1946 he suffered a coronary thrombosis, and had to be nursed. But Emma was now failing somewhat (she had had 6 teeth pulled the day before his attack) and had difficulty in finding nurses as they were superstitious about the 'head doctor', eventually finding two who did not know his reputation. Fortunately Jung did not become depressed after this episode. He continued to 'research' and to write books of a semi-mystical nature *'Aion'* in 1951, *'The Answer to Job'* in 1952, *'Psychology and Alchemy.'* And finally *'Mysterium Coniunctionis'*. In 1956 He saw few patients and only travelled about Switzerland.

On April 24th, 1948 the inaugural lecture of the C.G.Jung Institute of Zurich was given by Jung – ' expressing my particular pleasure and satisfaction that an Institute of Complex Psychology would carry on my work.' And giving tribute to all those who had helped him in his work.

Jung resigned in 1950 as President in 1950 and Emma took his place on the board. The classes were held in the house of the Psychological Club, in the Gemeindestrasse.

On March 21st, 1953, Toni Wolff, at the age of 65, was found dead in bed. She had been a heavy smoker all her life and no doubt had a coronary thrombosis. Jung was too upset to attend her funeral.

On November 25th, 1955 Jung wrote to Gerard Adler 'Frau Professor Jung is not well, not well at all'. She had been diagnosed with carcinoma of the stomach in 1952, and now had widespread metastases, with secondary deposits in the spine causing intense pain. In 1955 she had had chemotherapy and radiation treatment. On July 23rd, a celebration of Jung's 80th birthday was held, in accordance with Swiss custom which demands celebration of every 5th birthday after the 75th. Both were in high spirits. Emma's health deteriorated and she died on November 27th. She had been cared for by Ruth Bailey, whom Carl had met in Africa all those years ago, and was a true friend of the family and visited them regularly.

Following a family discussion about what was to be done with 'the old man', it was decide that Ruth Bailey would move into the house at Kusnacht to stay indefinitely. Jung soon regained his spirits and started carving stones again, with the inscription dedicated to Emma -She was the foundation of my house', to be placed in the tower at Bollingen.

Jung's book on Unidentified Flying Objects reached the largest audience and generated the greatest respect in his later years, published in 1958. **Charles Lindbergh** visited Jung at Bollinger and was unable to convince Jung that there was no objective evidence for the existence of UFOs but Jung refused to discuss it.

Jung had another heart attack in February 1960 and remained weak but his 85th birthday was celebrated on July 26th. in the usual custom. Later he collapsed on a journey to the Jura with severe stomach pains and returned home.

On May 17th, 1961 Jung had a stroke and his speech became unintelligible, but this later recovered to some extent. After a series of minor strokes, he died on June 6th, 1961.

Legend has it that a bolt of lightning destroyed the tree under which Jung would sit during his sessions, at the moment of his death. . There was a storm, but it did not strike till later. There was a thunderstorm on the morning of his funeral, June 9th. 'That's father grumbling,' remarked his daughter Agathe to Ruth Bailey.

— • —

Alfred Adler (1870-1937)

Adler was an Austrian psychiatrist who was originally an associate of Freud but disagreed with him over Freud's belief that sexuality was the prime motivator of human behaviour. He thought that need for superiority and power was, and formed his own school of individual psychiatry in 1911. He became President of the Vienna Psychoanalytic Society at the time.

Euglen Bleuler (1857 -1939)
Trained by Forel, he was director of the Cantonal Psychiatric University Hospital and Clinic of Zurich (the Burghölzli) at the time Jung presented himself as an intern. He was of peasant stock and the first member of his family to be educated beyond elementary school. He was described as a genuinely modest man 'motivated solely by a truly Christian ambition not to stand in the way of others, with a youthful eagerness to learn. His desire to study psychiatry could well have been motivated by the fact that his sister had a severe case of 'catatonic schizophrenia' and other members of his family were also afflicted.

The Burghölzli, prior to Bleuler's arrival, was simply a warehouse where mentally ill patients languished while the 'Directors' Griesinger, von Gudden and Hitzig, conducted 'research' that gained them an international reputation for them, and, by extension, for the hospital. These eminent doctors spoke only High German, which the average patient, speaking only his local dialect, could scarcely understand. Bleuler insisted that his doctors spoke in the local dialect, and socialised with them, much to their (the doctors) annoyance. One of his patients was the dancer Nijinski.

In 1911 Bleuler wrote a book *Dementia Praecox and the Schizophrenias* expanded and separated Kraepelin's ideas. He also coined the term *autism* to describe a key symptom in some of his patients.

Havelock Ellis (1859-1936)
He wrote a book called *Studies in the Psychology of Sex* outlining the new science of sexology in seven volumes. This provided a background to Freud's theories. Volume one was published in America in 1897, volume 7 also in America in 1928. Attempted publication in the UK led to the successful prosecution of the publisher, George Bedborough, in 1898, for 'obscene libel'.

Emil Kraepelin (1856-1926)
He attended the Universities of Warzberg, Munich and Leipzig, and at the latter came under the influence of Wilhelm Wundt (1832-1920) who had started the first Laboratory of Experimental Psychology in 1875, to take psychology away from the realm of speculation and to place it on a ration-

al basis. Kraepelin initially worked under Prof. **Von Gudden**, who drowned, together with his patient, the mad King Ludwig of Bavaria, in the Sternberg Lake. (Psychiatry can be a hazardous profession). In 1893 Kraepelin identified a condition in young patients which he called 'dementia praecox' to distinguish it from manic/depressive illness, and classified it into hebephrenic, catatonic and paranoid forms. Bleuler renamed it schizophrenia, as he did not think dementia was appropriete, in 1908.

Richard von Krafft Ebing

He wrote 'Psychopathia Sexualis in 1886. This contained alluring cases of sexual perversions and ran to 600 pages and 10 editions. He coined the term 'sadism' after the exploits of the writer Marquis de Sade and masochism after the writer Leopold Sacher- Masoch

II ABREACTION

Patients suffered nervous collapse and dysfunction following extreme trauma, life threatening events (*transmarginal inhibition*). This became evident during military service. A soldier would function appropriately during a battle, but would collapse afterwards – shell-shock as it was termed during World War I. The theory of the basis of treatment was that the patient could be 'cured' that is to say, normal function would be resumed, if the trauma could be relived with the associated emotion, which had been suppressed, fully expressed. The technique involved heavily sedating the patient with barbiturate, ether, or inducing a hypnotic trance, and getting him to relive the events that precipitated the collapse.

'The terror exhibited... is electrifying to watch. The body becomes increasingly tense and rigid; the eyes widen and the pupils dilate, while the skin becomes covered with a fine perspiration. The hands move convulsively... breathing becomes incredibly rapid and shallow. The intensity of the emotion sometimes becomes more than they can bear; and frequently at the height of the reaction, there is a collapse and the patient falls back in the bed and remains quiet for a few minutes.'

This was a description of abreaction under barbiturate of soldiers suffering acute collapse in the North African campaign in 1942 during World War II (Grinker and Spiegel quoted in Battle for the Mind). The stuporous becomes alert, the mute can talk. The deaf can hear, the paralysed can move, the terror-stricken psychotics become well organised individuals.

There is a curious similarity with religious conversion ceremonies. **John Wesley** (1703-1791), the founder of Methodism, was able to induce similar 'cures', though Wesley attributed these to the intervention of the Holy Ghost. A tremendous assault on the emotions was able to effect remarkable behavioural changes. John Wesley also believed in electro-therapy. A charged Leyden Jar was used to provide electric shocks, and was credited with many 'cures'. (He set up clinics in Moorfields, Southwark, St. Pauls and Seven Dials for this purpose in 1756). Similarly the Quakers, the Society of Friends , 'shook and trembled before the Lord'. 'Men women and little children at their meetings are strangely wrought upon their bodies, and brought to fall, foam at the mouth, roar and swell in their bellies.' The Quakers later settled down to become rich and respectable, abandoning the means by which they had built up their earlier spiritual strength. Religious sects lose the dynamism and enthusiasm of their founders with time, and repudiate the conversion techniques. Their leaders become organisation men and lose their power and influence. 'Fundamentalist' charismatic preachers have the ability to induce conversions. Such men are generally alpha-dominant males and are particularly attractive to females. Intellectual indoctrination without emotional excitement is remarkably ineffective.

In primitive societies such as the Voodoo culture of West Africa and Haiti, rhythmic drumming perhaps associated with drug taking, is used to induce the emotional assault necessary to effect the desired transformation and submission to the God, that is , to the Chief. In the initiation rites of the tribes of New Guinea, adolescent boys are circumcised whilst in a trance, before being accepted as full members of the tribe.(Sir James Frazer, *The Golden Bough*).

The conversion of **St Paul** on the road to Damascus may well have been a similar instance. After an acute stage of nervous excitement he was struck blind and only after three days indoctrination by Ananias did he recover his sight and become one of the driving forces leading to the establishment of Christianity as a dominant religion.(Acts of the Apostles Chapter IX, probably written by St Luke, a physician.).

III. COGNITIVE ANALYTIC THERAPY

In this context Cognitive means Thinking as opposed to Knowing. Patients or clients are referred from the Accident and Emergency units of the Hospital having overdosed, or detoxication units, – and put on the 'waiting list' for therapy. The common factor is self-harm and many suffer from

Borderline Personality Disorder (see Diagnosis -Chapter 2) with a history of childhood abuse. It is as though the 'computer' of the brain has been wrongly programmed, or corrupted by a virus, which leads to erroneous thought patterns and inappropriate behaviour, particularly violence directed against the self or others. The object of therapy is to correct the thoughts and to eliminate the aggressive behaviour patterns and enable the sufferer to lose his alienation and return to the human race. The virus that has entered their souls cause disputes and disagreements to be settled, not by reason, but by violence. This may or may not be possible.

A 'contract' is established with the patient. A course of 16 weekly sessions is arranged with the therapist. The patient must agree to:

1. No drugs except as prescribed by a doctor.
2. No excess drinking.
3. No violence or threatening behaviour. (Psychiatrists and therapists have been murdered by their patients. Proper protection must always be available and given.)

A document must be signed to this effect.

The objects of treatment are Reformulation, Recognition, Revision. At the first meeting the patient is given a Psychotherapy File, which he takes away and is used for self-monitoring, identifying dilemmas, traps and snags. He must record his daily thoughts and feelings, for discussion in subsequent sessions. A Personality Assessment Schedule, is to be completed, giving his assessment and memories of his early life and relationships with parents, siblings, illnesses, and attitude to work in the family, and degrees of expressed emotion. Some people can express themselves better in painting and drawing than words. Sometimes painful memories have been repressed, and have to be explored very tactfully. The therapist has to identify the conflicts that lead to alienation, and try to correct the inappropriate thoughts that lead to inappropriate words and actions, of which there are three:

1.The world is dangerous and malevolent.
2. I am powerless and vulnerable.
3. I am inherently unacceptable.

Many Borderline Personality Disorder patients use anger to conceal or defend vulnerability. At the end of the sessions, 'goodbye' letters are written both by the therapist and, hopefully, the patient, indicating the termination of the relationship. However, an appointment is given for 3 months' time so as not to make the break too painful.

'Of a total of well over 2000 outpatients treated with Cognitive Analytic Therapy at St. Thomas' and Guy's Hospitals, of whom at least 10% met borderline (BPD) criteria, only 4 died by suicide during or shortly after their therapy. Of these, 3 were borderline patients associated with bi-polar affective disorder, and all were inpatients at the time of death.' (Ryle) The death of psychiatric patients is extremely stressful for those concerned, and therapists need much support. Relatives are prone to blame those involved, so they must be warned in advance of the possibility and hopefully to avoid litigation, which is expensive, prolonged, and demoralising.

IV. COGNITIVE BEHAVIOUR THERAPY
This is directed to correcting disordered or inappropriate thoughts, erroneous beliefs, which cause anxiety and/or depression. Behaviour therapy means unlearning a bad habit.

'The therapist helps the patient to identify his warped thinking and to learn more realistic ways to formulate his experiences.' (Beck – 1989) The therapist must establish credibility (transference) and adopt a neutral emotional stance. He or she must not try to correct delusional systems prematurely before such transference has been established. The theory is that patients have persistent 'automatic thoughts' (called by Plato 'internal dialogue') which must be viewed objectively and assessed for their reality content with the object of reducing their emotional content.

The patient is allocated graded tasks and to record his automatic thoughts, and to assess their reality content and to discuss these with the therapist during subsequent sessions. It may take from 10 to 20 weekly sessions to achieve success.

Behaviour therapy involves 'desensitising' a patient to the phobic situation by training him or her to relax during the perceived danger, and get the patient to realise that they are reacting to an imaginary danger rather than a real one. Another technique is 'role playing' to improve assertiveness and to get them to improve their self confidence.

Cognitive Behaviour Therapy dispenses with the symbolic, concentrates on the actual, and concepts such as the superego, ego and id are abandoned, together with the unconscious.

Therapists try to make their disciplines 'scientific' and therefore respectable, and CBT is said to be comprehensive, testable, teachable and economic in terms of time and money. Unfortunately they are dealing with the subjective, not the objective, and scientific method cannot truly be applied as there can never be 'control' or matched untreated patients, particularly suicidal ones.

CBT has been used to try to get criminals to mend their ways, with remarkably little success. This is hardly surprising considering that most criminals suffer from personality disorder, are compulsive liars (called street cred) and are totally lacking in empathy, having no consideration for the feelings of their victims.

V. ELECTRO CONVULSIVE TREATMENT – ECT

Electric shock treatment has a long and venerable history. In ancient Greece physicians would use electricity derived from the electric torpedo fish or cramp-fish, common in the Mediterranean, especially for headaches.

In the 18th century electricity derived from friction machines such as the Wilmshurst machine to provide shocks, later supplanted by Leyden Jars, which could store electricity, and provide some measure of control of the dose and was used for relief of local pain and for paralysis. . Fairground men would charge sixpence for punters to be 'electrified out of their senses'.

In 1793 an Electrical Dispensary was set up at St. Thomas' Hospital in London 'with a view to afford a new benefit to the lower orders of Mankind.' In that year 3,274 patients were treated, 1401 cured, and 1,232 relieved. (C.A. Highmore – *pietas Londinensis*, 1810). **Benjamin Franklin** had a shock which knocked him to the ground, rendering him unconscious, with retrograde amnesia, and suggested it be tried on 'mad people.' It was successfully used by Mr **John Birch**, surgeon, at St. Thomas' for melancholics, with electrodes applied to the head.

In 1938 **U. Cerletti** and **L. Bini** in Rome introduced electroconvulsive treatment in cases of severe depression. It had been noted that epileptic patients with depression experienced a relief of symptoms following a convulsion.

In certain cases of acute depression with marked suicidal tendencies and melancholia, ECT is indicated by virtue of its rapid response. Most pharmacological treatments may take two or three weeks to become effective and can be started when the patient is improving. It is indicated in puerperal depression or psychosis, in order to keep mother and baby together. Generally 2 – 3 treatments per week are given, and, depending on response, 4 – 8 treatments. It is said to be effective in uncontrollable mania due to cocaine overdose.

An epileptic fit is induced by passing an electric current though the brain. When it was first introduced it caused considerable trauma, both physical (broken bones – especially vertebral), and psychological, terrifying, painful and humiliating, and patients were reluctant to accept it – problems of 'valid consent' arose. Nowadays it is done under light general anaesthesia with a muscle relaxant. An electric current is passed through the non-dominant side of the brain -the right side in the case of right handed people. One of the 'side effects' of this form of treatment is memory loss, similar to concussion, and unilateral ECT minimises this loss.

Its indication in schizophrenia is questionable. Patients may well become depressed (schizo-affective disorder) because their brain isn't working properly and they cannot get on with their lives, but it probably does not influence the basic psycho-pathology of the condition. Also in anxiety and obsessional states it may make the symptoms worse.

VI. INSULIN COMA THERAPY
'Shock' treatment was used in the treatment of acute schizophrenic breakdown. One of the means of inducing shock was to put the patient into a hypoglycaemic coma using insulin. In 1933 **Manfred Sakel** of Vienna presented a report. The coma lasted about an hour, after which intravenous glucose was used to terminate it. There seems to be little physiological basis for this treatment, merely 'empirical'. It was probably a form of abreaction.

VII. LEUCOTOMY
(Lobotomy) See under Chapter 5, Psychosurgery.

CHAPTER FIVE

PSYCHO-PHARMACOLOGY

The Search for 'Soma' ('Soma' was the universal panacea for all unhappiness as described by Aldous Huxley in his book *Brave New World*)

The search for tranquillity and pain relief is as old as Mankind. Drugs foster a kind of Nirvana in which 'Man is able to lose his futile individuality in the mystic ecstasy of universal life under the Dionysiac spell of music, rhythm and dance' (Nietzsche). The American Indians with their peyote, and modern jazz musicians with their marijuana have discovered this. The trouble is, it doesn't last, and sooner or later, the real world intrudes, and the pot-heads are ill equipped to cope. The problem then is that they have become detached from reality, that is to say, other people.

The notion that drugs can be classified as stimulants and sedatives is not wholly true. Depending on circumstances, they can be either or both. What is a stimulant to one person may be a sedative to another. Terms like 'tranquillizer' have been invented by drug houses to sell their wares. Even the word 'drug' has a negative connotation, suggesting illegal substances. In the USA a 'drug store' is now a 'pharmacy.' Overdose of many drugs leads to coma and convulsions, minimal and maximal stimulus at the same time. In this section, therefore, groups of drugs are classified alphabetically, rather than by their alleged pharmacological activity.

The production and sale of 'remedies' has always been a profitable business and now, with 'science' to the rescue, it has become exceedingly so, and the 'drug houses' and their owners, have become very wealthy. Many, such as Ciba-Geigy, Hoffman La Roche, Sandoz and Hoeschst are based in Switzerland. But their research activities have produced many useful products.

1. Alcohol

Drink, Sir, is a great Provoker…….
Lechery, Sir, it Provokes and Unprovokes. It Provokes the Desire, But it takes away the performance.

(Macbeth -Act 2, Scene3)

A BRIEF HISTORY OF PSYCHIATRY

Malt does more than Milton can,
To justify God's ways to Man.

A. E. Housman

The fermentation products of grapes have been known and used from antiquity. Many other plants, seeds, and fruits containing glycogen, or its degradation product glucose, can be fermented by enzymes to produce alcohol. In the case of beer, barley is used, as it is for whisky, which is distilled to increase its alcohol content. Beer contains about 5% alcohol, wine about 10-15% alcohol, whisky and gin about 40% alcohol, vodka even more. On reaching the brain, it interferes with the neuro transmitter system, leading to euphoria, disinhibition, impaired judgment, and slowed up reflex activity, rendering driving cars extremely dangerous.

It is a socially acceptable drug, highly esteemed, one drinks to the Health, indeed essential for parties, sanctified in the Christian Religion in the Communion Service. But in Islam it is strictly forbidden.

But it is a poisoner and an ensnarer. Tolerance and addiction can occur. It can cause cirrhosis of the liver, heart and nerve damage, pancreatitis and dementia. It can damage an unborn baby (foetal alcohol syndrome.) It is said to be a cause of cancer. It is said to be implicated in 40-50% of fatal road traffic accidents in the US, as well as other accidental causes of death, drowning, fire, and falls. It can be implicated in homicide and suicide.

It may take 20-30 years of steady drinking before morning shakes appear, which can only be alleviated by another drink. It is said that 6% of men and 2% of women will become alcohol dependent. A mournful litany of a temperance lecture. But wrecked lives, wrecked marriages, lost jobs, is the heavy price to be paid.

Attempts to reduce its availability and consumption by rationing, taxation or prohibition have not been successful. The Volstead Act of 1919 in the USA, caused a temporary reduction in availability but it led to such widespread illicit production and racketeering that it was abandoned in 1931. In the USA state and federal taxation produced $18 Billion annually in 2000, and proportional amounts are raised in the UK, which makes Governments drink dependent for their revenue. In England, many brewers, having become extremely wealthy, and having given generous donations to the ruling political party, have been elevated to the House of Lords – the Beerage. (see also Addiction, Chapter 3).

2. Amphetamine

This is a synthetic stimulant similar in its effects to cocaine, and with a chemical structure similar to adrenaline (epinephrine in the US). It was originally used as a nasal decongestant but this use has been superseded by ephedrine. It has been used an antidepressant, but only turned the patient into someone who was not only depressed but anxious, and there was a strong possibility of addiction, so it is no longer used in this connection.

It can keep people awake and was used in World War II in aircrews, it was the 'stirrup-cup of the Panzers'. Long-distance truck drivers have been known to take it, and dance bands could play all night.

It is also an appetite suppressant, and various derivatives have been used as slimming aids, but they soon lose their effect and it is not considered good practice. It does, however, have a legitimate use in the treatment of *narcolepsy*, a condition in which a person can have an overwhelming desire to sleep at inopportune moments.

Another derivative, *Methylphenidate (Ritalin)* is used in the treatment of ADHD, Attention Deficit Hyperactivity Syndrome, in children. In America it is said that sometimes 20% of the children in certain classes are on it, and some are genuinely helped, but it is thought by many that it is inappropriate to medicalise what may well be a social problem of maladjustment – the quick fix.

Amphetamine and its methylated derivative (d-desoxyephedrine) *methedrine* – methamphetamine *(speed)* have become drugs of addiction, and there have been cases of amphetamine psychosis. This occurred in 1968 when the supply of heroin by certain private doctors was cut off because a law was passed that only doctors with a special Home Office licence could supply heroin. Special Drug Dependence Units were set up in an attempt to manage the epidemic of heroin addicts. Unfortunately, these private doctors immediately switched to prescribing ampoules of methedrine, and an epidemic of methedrine addicts appeared especially in Camberwell. This was stopped by the drug manufacturers agreeing to withdraw all samples from retail pharmacies, supplies only being available from hospital pharmacies. This epidemic soon stopped, but it was succeeded by the druggies finding solace in injected barbiturates, and further supplies of black-market heroin

Another amphetamine derivative is the recreational drug *Ecstasy*, which is chemically 3,4, methylene dioxy metamphetamine (MDMA), the dance drug of choice on account of its stimulant and 'closeness' properties – 'the champagne of the feeling enhancers'. It was first synthesised by Merck in 1912, but not until the 1970s was it used in conjunction with psychotherapy. In 1985 its dangers were recognised and was put under strict control by both the US Drug Enforcement Agency (DEA) and similarly in the UK. The first ecstasy death was recorded in 1988, and now there are said to be 40 deaths a year. One of the lethal side effects is hyperthermia, in which the body temperature rises to 109 deg F., (normal 98.4), with hallucinations, collapse, convulsions and heart failure. Long term use may cause brain damage with memory impairment.

Starting about 1990, metamphetamine (known as 'Ya ba or Mad Medicine') smoking has unfortunately reached epidemic proportions in parts of the Asia/Pacific region. It is easily manufactured with apparatus carried on the back of a truck. In Thailand 83 million tablets were seized in 2002. Villages which historically were opium territory now turned to metamphetamine.

3. Barbiturates

Alcohol and opium and various other herbal remedies have since time immemorial been used for their sedative properties, including henbane, valerian, St John's Wort, etc. and with the development of chemical synthesis in the 19th century the search began for more 'scientific' remedies, which could be assayed and standardised. Bromides became fashionable, then chloral hydrate, and in 1903 *barbitone* was synthesised. The derivatives, barbiturates, were effective anti-convulsants, and were used as anaesthetic agents and hypnotics, for insomnia. They became very widely used but patients became dependent on them and experienced severe withdrawal symptoms, including convulsions and delirium tremens, similar to alcohol. In the 1950s there were 5000-7000 cases of barbiturate overdoses and in 1967 over 2000 deaths in the UK from overdose, deliberate or accidental. In the 1960s it was estimated that 100.000 people were dependent on them.

They became 'street drugs,' with widespread abuse and racketeering before heroin overtook them. But while a heroin addict is passive, a barbiturate addict can become extremely violent and could die from overdose. But in the 1960s, with the introduction of the benzodiezepines, barbiturate use progressively declined, and is now mainly an anaesthetic drug.

4. Benzodiazepines

In the 1930s Dr **Leo Sternbach** was a chemist working at the University of Cracow, Poland. He started synthesising benzodiazepines out of curiosity more than anything. In 1954 he was working in the laboratories of Hoffman La Roche in New Jersey USA, and decided to test these drugs for pharmacological activity, using experimental animals. They showed no activity so he abandoned the study. 18 months later he tried a left-over sample coded Ro 5-0690 and when tested, it was found to have remarkable sedative activity. It was called *Librium*. A later derivative was called *Valium*.

(Librium is generically *benzodiazepoxide* and Valium is *diazepine*). Roche (a private company) made a fortune as these two drugs became best-sellers and rectal valium is still the drug of choice for *status epilepticus*. *Nitrazepine* (*Mogadon*) was a widely used hypnotic.

Pharmacologically, they appear to potentiate the action of the sedative GABA (gamma-amino-butyric acid) as opposed to the stimulant dopamine. But tolerance develops when used in high doses. The normal dose of Valium is 2 milligrams, but when 10 milligrams is used there is a serious risk of addiction, with its unpleasant withdrawal symptoms. *Ativan* was the most likely to lead to dependence. Their great advantage it they are not lethal even in high doses, unlike the barbiturates, though when mixed with alcohol they can be lethal. By 1970 they had almost supplanted barbiturates and there were said to be about a million people taking them long term in the UK, and world wide were the most frequently prescribed drug.

By 1980, a backlash had developed as increasing numbers of people became addicted but by then litigation culture had developed and many people started instructing their lawyers to sue doctors and manufacturers for alleged negligence in the matter. At one time over 100 litigants banded together to sue the manufacturers, unsuccessfully.

5 Cannabis

Hashish, Marijuana, pot, grass, ganja, etc etc. (*Cannabis Sativa* and *Cannabis Indica*).

cartoon by Matt courtesy *Daily Telegraph*

Indian Hemp grows widely in temperate and semi-tropical countries, and was used to make sacks and rope. Another use was as a mind-altering substance. The active principal is *tetrahydrocannabinol*. It is drug of great antiquity, recognised in China in 3000 BC. It has been used for its analgesic, local anaesthetic, anti-depressant, and antibiotic activity. . It has been used in religious ceremonies by the Rastafarians. It also causes euphoria, a feeling of well-being, and therefore has been condemned by modern Western-type governments, in fact made illegal. This has led to a vast trade in its manufacture, distribution and marketing, and, due to its illegality, straight into the hands of the criminal classes, with all its associated blackmail, corruption and racketeering. Many dubious characters have become extremely wealthy. The notion that 'the law' can stop people medicating themselves is untenable. 'The Law' only applies to the law-abiding, probably 99% of the population, but it seems a shame to turn the erstwhile law-abiding into criminals, merely because they wish to indulge in smoking cannabis. The notion that it causes 'mental illness' is questionable. Most probably it is the 'mentally ill' who take cannabis for relief of their distress, perhaps to ease the torment of living in a dreary dismal unprofitable world. But like all psychoactive substances, overdose can cause hallucinations and a psychotic like state. The word 'assassin' has been thought to derive from those whose aggression was caused by Hashish. It has been used medicinally for the treatment of neuralgic pains in MS (Multiple Sclerosis).

In 1998 health officials in Geneva suppressed the publication of a politically sensitive analysis that confirms what aging hippies have known for decades: cannabis is safer than tobacco or alcohol. The analysis concludes not only that the amount of dope smoked worldwide does less harm than drink or cigarettes but that the same is likely to hold true even if people consumed dope on the same scale as these legal substances. The comparison was due to appear in a report on the harmful effects of cannabis published in December 1997 by the WHO, but it is understood to have been dropped after the US National Institute on Drug Abuse and the UN International Drug Control Programme warned that it would play into the hands of groups campaigning to legalise marijuana. (Geographical May1998)

6. Cocaine

A drug found in the leaves of the South American coca bush – *Erythroxylum coca,* growing in the Andes best at 1000 -2 000 metres elevation, primarily in Columbia, Peru, Ecuador, Bolivia and Brazil. It is a powerful stimulant, chewed by the natives to give them endurance for the hard work in the fields and silver mines.

In 1860 a German chemist, **Albert Niemann**, isolated the drug as cocaine hydrochloride. Pharmacologically, it appears to interfere with dopamine transport in the brain. It causes intense euphoria and a rush of pleasure, but it is a drug of dependence, and high doses cause confusion and paranoia, with hallucinations of bugs crawling under the skin (formication – from the Latin *formica,* an ant).

In 1884 **Sigmund Freud** became interested in the drug and used it on himself noting its euphoriant effect, and sent some to his fiancée Martha Bernhays. Before long he was taking regular doses of it himself, calling it a 'magic drug', thinking it could be used as a cure for morphine dependence, with disastrous results.

An Austrian doctor, **Karl Koller**, an ophthalmologist, noted that his tongue became numb when touched by cocaine, and in 1884 gave a lecture in Heidelberg illustrating that it could be used as a local anaesthetic, particularly in eye operations. This was a major advance, and many operations are now done under local anaesthetic, using derivatives of cocaine such as procaine, lignocaine (xylocaine) amethocaine, etc., as nerve blocking agents or local skin anaesthetics. The problem with cocaine is that some people are sensitive to it, develop anaphylactic shock and can die of cardiac arrythmias, so the drug is no longer used in medicine.

It is used recreationally by sniffing up the nose, which produces an immediate effect, less dangerous then injection, but tolerance and dependence results. It may well be carcinogenic over a long period of time.

In 1970, crack cocaine was introduced, by which the cocaine base was split off by heating with an alkali such as sodium bicarbonate. This produced 'freebase' cocaine, which could be smoked.

Attempts to regulate the trade in cocaine have not been successful, owing to the immense profits to be made.

The economics of cocaine is a heady brew of crime, morality, politics and pharmacology. The Coca farmers' plight is unenviable. He gets very little for his crop. It is periodically sprayed with toxic defoliant at the behest of, and paid for, by the Americans in their bizarre 'War on Drugs' – quite unwinnable of course. The price of a manufactured Kilogram of Cocaine is said to be £500. The street price is £5000. Periodic seizures of consignments of cocaine by well meaning customs officials merely puts up the price rendering trafficking even more profitable. But there is evidence now that the street price of cocaine – £35 a gram, is actually falling.

The fact that possession of the drug is illegal renders immense opportunities for blackmail, amongst police and customs officers especially, leading to widespread corruption and demoralisation amongst staff.

The insatiable desire of *homo sapiens* for pleasure is the driving force behind its consumption. But it is a dangerous drug – anaphylaxis and cardiotoxicity can cause death. Sigmund Freud was addicted to both cocaine and nicotine (cigars), the former causing his weird ideas (sexual) and the latter his death from cancer of the mouth. 'Desire is the cause of all unhappiness' say the Buddhists and the Christian ethic is expressed the Lord's prayer – 'Lead us not into Temptation'. The problem then is a moral one. Treating it as a criminal one does not work. The jails are awash with drugs. The solution is to be sought in proper upbringing, encouraging a sense of responsibility – too much welfare encourages fatherless families. Restoration of the nuclear family as ideal should be done. It will take time.

Heroin addiction is different from cocaine. Total moral anarchy develops. The craving is intense. The addict will murder with no remorse to obtain his fix. Many heroin addicts have suffered childhood abuse, and need to have their self-esteem restored. This is time consuming and expensive, but must not be regarded as impossible.

7. Khat (also known as qat, quat, mira etc.)
This is derived from a shrub that grows in the Northern Highlands of Ethiopia and Somalia – *Catha edulis forrskal*, named in honour of the 18th century botanist **Peter Forrskal** who brought it back to Europe. The plant material is taken into the mouth and chewed. Often there is group activity, in the Room of Peace, in a semi-religious setting, as its use brings a sense of trust, contentment, excitement and wisdom. Soon the party becomes increasingly frenetic, over-excited, and no-one sleeps that night.

The active ingredient is the highly unstable *cathionone*, which appears to have amphetamine like activity.

Custom and manners control its use, which is predominately in Muslim countries, in which alcohol is forbidden. Various attempts have been made to ban it, but with little success. It is said that 7 tonnes a week are flown into Heathrow, quite legally, some for onward shipment, some for local consumption by Somalis and other refugees.

Betel nut chewing is another custom particularly in Asian countries, as a mild stimulant, but again may well be carcinogenic over prolonged use.

8. Lithium
The success of lithium in the treatment of manic-depressive (bipolar) illness was first described by Dr **John Cade** in the *Medical Journal of Australia* in September 1949. A male patient, W.B., aged 57 who was manic, destructive, uncooperative, restless and 'the most troublesome patient in the ward' was treated with lithium and discharged from hospital and back to his job after 3 months treatment, with instructions to continue treatment, and to take his tablets twice weekly. He soon stopped his medication and relapsed, requiring readmission, but improved again when it was restarted.

The story of this discovery is quite remarkable. With experience of three

119

and a half years in a Japanese prisoner of war camp, Cade wondered if the condition of some of his patients was due to poisoning by some chemical. After the war he returned to become medical superintendent of the Repatriation Hospital in Bundoora, a suburb of Melbourne. He injected urine of some of his most disturbed patients into guinea-pigs to see if there was some toxic substance causing their illness. All the guinea pigs died. Nothing daunted, he tried to determine which component of the urine was responsible, testing urea, uric acid and creatinine. Uric acid is somewhat insoluble so he substituted Lithium Urate. Then he decided to inject lithium urate alone. 'After a period of about two hours, the animals, although fully conscious, became unresponsive to stimuli... those who have experimented with guinea pigs know to what extent a 'startle' reaction is part of their make-up. It was even more startling to Dr Cade to find that after the injection they could be turned on their backs and that, instead of their usual frantic behaviour, they merely lay there and gazed placidly back at him.'

After a fortnight's self administration to investigate toxicity, Cade gave the drug to 19 patients, 10 with mania, 6 with schizophrenia, and 3 with psychotic depression. It had no effect on depressives, slightly calmed the schizophrenics, but had an extraordinary effect on mania, as described above, on W.B.

But it was another 20 years before it became generally known, and used. First, the Medical Journal of Australia was not widely read. A British psychiatrist. **Dr David Rice**, was in charge of Graylingwell Hospital, Chichester, in 1952-3. He had two particularly difficult and over-reactive patients to whom he would liked to have given ECT, but the relatives forbade it. An Australian registrar, who happened to be standing by when Dr Rice was pondering what to do, produced a crumpled sheet from the Medical Journal of Australia, containing Cade's article. Dr Rice felt he had nothing to lose, so he tried it, with some diffidence, as it was believed lithium was extremely toxic.(Fortunately Dr Cade was unaware of this) with effect.

From 1952, a young Danish psychiatrist **Mogens Schou**, who himself suffered from manic depressive illness, as did his family, was greatly helped and championed the use of lithium, but it was not licenced for use in the USA until 1970. It is quite toxic, (kidney damage) and blood levels have to be monitored.

The effectiveness of lithium is important from a theoretical point of view, in that much of what is believed to be psychological in origin, may in fact be metabolic. The condition of Seasonal Affective Disorder (SAD), in which some people get severely depressed in winter time, may be a hormonal response, related to the occurrence of hibernation in some animals.

In addition, enlargement of the thyroid gland occurs in 5% of patients on lithium, and 20% of women on lithium develop hypothyroidism with a compensatory rise in Thyroid Stimulating Hormone derived from the anterior pituitary gland. Sometimes there is coarsening of the hair and hair loss. It may be necessary to add throxine to compensate for this. ECG changes may occur due to displacement of potassium by lithium in the myocardium. It would appear that lithium has an effect on the pituitary/hypothalamic axis, which may explain its activity in manic/depressive disorder.

9. MAOIs

Mono-amine-oxidase inhibitors. The discovery of these, the first anti-depressants, was an amazing example of serendipity. What happened was that patients under treatment for pulmonary tuberculosis, in the 1950s, when given the usual 'Triple Therapy', consisting of streptomycin, PAS (para-amino-salicylic acid), and INH (isoniazid) became very cheerful and elated. Investigation proved that this was due to the INH, and further investigation led to the discovery that pharmacologically, it was an inhibitor of the enzyme mono-amine oxidase.

This left increasing amounts of the stimulant neurotransmitter L-tryptamine in the brain with anti-depressant effects. Nardil and Parnate were among the first commercially available drugs. Unfortunately when taken with certain foods containing *tyramine* such as blue cheese, serious hypertension resulted with the occurrence of strokes, and they fell from grace.

10. Mescaline

'Their properties of evoking sense-illusions in a great variety of forms, of giving rise in the human soul as if by magic to apparitions whose brilliant, seductive, perpetually changing aspects produce a rapture which is incessantly renewed and in comparison with which the perceptions of consciousness are but pale shadows. Harmonious vibrations of sounds beyond all human belief are heard, phantasms appear before men's eyes as if they were real, offered to them as a gift from almighty God.' (**Louis Lewin**, German pharmacologist 1931).

The *hallucinogens* are drugs which can cause a wide variety of mental effects. LSD (Lysergic acid diethylamide) is active in minute (microgram) doses, with high degrees of tolerance developing, but no withdrawal symptoms. It is present in the seeds of Morning Glory (*Ipomea*) and the fly agaric mushroom, *Amanita muscaria*. But the major source is the Central American *Peyote Cactus*, yielding *Mescaline*. But response to the drug is uncertain, and conditioning helps – expectation. A 'bad trip' may result in a storm of disoriented terror, hideous visions and hell let loose. In such circumstances, people may harm themselves or others. A bad trip may last for a few hours, talking to a friend may help to restore a sense of reality, but sometimes hospital admission is required. Death is unlikely unless the taker believes he can fly and jumps out of out a window.

In the 16th century the natives of Mexico were found by the Spanish conquistadores to be taking extracts of the peyote cactus for religious and magical purposes. The Spanish priests tried to suppress it, and extracted confessions, believing it to be ungodly. But the practice has outlived the conquistadores and was found to be alive and flourishing in the 19th and 20th centuries. But its use was constrained by ritual. The people would go out into the desert to find the '*flesh of the gods*' and would fast and abstain from sex to purify themselves. On returning, the people would sit in a circle, drums would beat, and the shaman would hand each person a portion of peyote, and everyone would enter the spirit world. Private consumption was strictly forbidden. The sacred mushrooms of Mexico were called 'God's flesh' by the Aztecs. It is interesting to reflect that, in the Eucharist or Communion Service of High Church Christians, especially Catholics, the Body of Christ is said to be eaten, symbolically in the form of a wafer. This notion presumably must have been derived from an earlier religious custom.

In the 1930s, a research chemist at Sandoz Laboritaries, Dr **Albert Hoffman**, while working on a substance derived from the fungus *ergot*, which grows on rye, isolated LSD, lysergic acid diethylamide. Taking up the investigation again in 1943, he suddenly found himself in a dream world, a kaleidoscope of colours, 'a strange but not unpleasant condition.' He went home, but suspecting that there might have been another cause for his experience, he took another dose the next day, this time by mouth. But the effect was anything but pleasant, everything became grotesque, he was seized with a dreadful fear of becoming insane and thought he might be dying. The drug was taken up by many gurus, cult figures and psychiatrists as a cure for schizophrenia. It was advanced as a cure for alcoholism, depression, psychopathy, sexual deviation, autism etc. – in fact LSD was the latest wonder drug. The word 'psychedelic' was coined by a Canadian psychiatrist Dr **Humphrey Osmond**, who introduced the writer **Aldous Huxley** to mescaline, and Huxley later wrote 'The Doors of Perception' as a result of his experiences.

But the chief protagonist – the High Priest – was Dr **Timothy Leary**, a psychologist who held a Chair at Harvard University. He had Huxley, Allen Ginsberg, William Burroughs, Arthur Koestler as his subjects. In 1963 he administered LSD to 10 theology students in a Boston University Chapel, which produced a startling spectacle. One student thought he was a fish. Leary set up an LSD commune in Mexico, lost his job at Harvard, was expelled from Mexico, and was convicted by the US authorities on drugs charges. He claimed that LSD was the best ever aphrodisiac. One of the side effects of LSD is that episodes of odd thought and behaviour can occur long after the drug had been taken, and LSD fell into disrepute

In 1964 LSD, psilocybin and mescaline were controlled by the Misuse of Substances Act in the UK. Legislation followed in 1965 in the US. In 1966 California outlawed the manufacture, supply and possession of LSD, and Federal legislation followed in 1968.

It still remains an illicit street drug, the teenage clubbers world, in doses of about 100 micrograms – a microdot, enabling the user to dance the night away, along with *ketamine, ecstasy, cannabis, PCP (Angel Dust)* and *Rohypnol,* the date rape drug with a rapid sedative action and an evil reputation.

11. Nicotine

Tobacco was brought to Europe by the sailors of Christopher Columbus in 1492. His men had observed the natives smoking the rolled up leaves of a plant, especially *nicotiana tabacum*. Today, according to a World Bank report, there are across the globe, 1.1 billion people, one third of adults, smoking. It causes a feeling of pleasure and relaxation though first exposure can induce nausea. It appears to be one of the few drugs of addiction that does not make people economic with the truth. One can get a truthful answer to a question with regard to cigarette consumption. But not with alcohol or other drugs which tends to be denied or minimised.

Nicotine is a drug of dependence, with unpleasant withdrawal symptoms, and being carcinogenic, and can be said to be the major cause of preventable, premature and unpleasant death today.

It is usually smoked, but can sniffed up the nose in the form of snuff, popular in the 17th and 18th centuries but not today.

12. Opium (including morphine and heroin)
Opium is derived from the poppy, *papaver somniferum,* originally native of Turkey, but now largely cultivated in the Himalayas and the Golden Triangle of Burma, Afghanistan Pakistan and Thailand, whose economies depend on it. The milky juice is obtained by incising the unripe poppy seed. The active alkaloids are concentrated by repeated boiling and evaporating. It is a drug of great antiquity. Poppy heads have been found in a Neolithic burial cave at Albunoz, Southern Spain, dated 4,200 BC.

Its use was described by the Greek Physician **Dioscorides** in the first Century A.D. in his work 'De Materia Medica', and it became the leading analgesic drug. In middle ages in the form of *paregoric* (camphorated tincture of opium) it was used for diarrhoea and the stronger *laudanum* was for febrile illnesses and for pain relief.

In 1788 **Warren Hastings**, first Governor-General of India, described opium as 'a pernicious article of luxury which ought not to be permitted but for the purpose of foreign commerce only.'

Thus began the 'foreign commerce' whereby opium was exported to China from India in exchange for silk, causing immense problems to the Chinese who tried to suppress it, resulting in the Opium Wars of the mid 19th century.

The problem with opium, and its active ingredient *morphine* and its acetylated derivative *heroin*, is that it is extremely addictive, with a development of tolerance, in that increasing doses are necessary to obtain the desired effect, that is to say, euphoria and oblivion.

It can be smoked, taken by mouth, or, for rapid relief, injected. With the invention of the hypodermic syringe about 1850, huge numbers of addicts were created in the aftermath of the American Civil War. The side effects include anorexia, increasing constipation, and respiratory inhibition, leading to death. Pin-point pupils are characteristic of the morphine taker.

Codeine (morphine methyl ether) is a derivative of morphine, with less sedative activity, but more constipating, and is used in bowel upsets.

13. Phenothazines

It was noted that anti-histamines had sedative side effects, and manipulation of the molecules led to the discovery of *chlorpromazine (Largactil)* in the early 1950s, with pronounced sedative action without inhibiting respiration.

In 1952 the French psychiatrists **Jean Delay** and **Pierre Deniker** treated a schizophrenic 57 year old labourer with chlorpromazine and after 2 weeks he was well enough to be discharged from hospital. This revolutionised the treatment of patients, especially those suffering from mania, as an injection of 100 milligrams of Largactil could effectively sedate them without putting their life in danger. This, in turn, associated with other medications, led to the realisation that the large institutional mental hospitals were no longer necessary, and led to their closure, to be replaced by 'care in the community' with a different set of consequences.

Hans Eyzenck, in his book 'The Effects of Psychotherapy: an Evaluation.' noted that there was no objective evidence for the therapeutic efficacy of Freudian psychotherapy, and **Edwin Shorter** commented that 'Freuds' ideas, which had dominated psychiatry for the first half of the century, were now vanishing like the snows of last winter'.

The *tricyclics* are phenothiazine derivatives and were introduced in the 1950s and were widely used. They include Amitryptiline (Tryptizole) and Nortryptiline. They are said to take 2-3 weeks of treatment before becoming effective but have unpleasant side effects such as a dry mouth and Parkinsonian type tremor and rigidity.

The phenothiazines have an even more unfortunate side effect than dry mouth. It is *tardive dyskinesia*, a condition in which the patient suffers involuntary athetoid, writhing shaking movements, especially of the face, head and neck, sometimes affecting the limbs. This can arise after a few weeks' treatment, and can take many months to subside, if at all. An early indication of toxicity is fine tremor of the tongue. There is some evidence that patients taking *respiridone* are more alert and responsive than those on chlorpromazine.

But maintaining people with schizophrenia on neuroleptics may actually be doing them a disservice. According to a 50 year review, long term treatment worsens long term prognosis and up to 40% of people would do better without them. Helping patients who are stabilised to gradually withdraw them would increase recovery rates and reduce the proportion of patients who become chronically ill.(Medical Hypotheses – 2004). This become evident in the case of the American schizophrenic mathematician **John Nash** who recovered and went on to win the Nobel Prize for economics with his 'game theory'. He refused to take his medication and was sustained by the love of his wife, so that his 'domain' had not disappeared. (*A Beautiful Mind*- by Sylvia Nasar)

14. SSRIs

Selective serotonin reuptake inhibitors. The current 'anti'depressants'.

Serotonin is chemically 5-hydroxy-tryptamine. This as a neurotransmitter associated with stimulant activity in the brain, and when its destruction is blocked, accumulates, with anti-depressant activity.

SSRIs include *fluoxetine* (Prozac). In 2002, 5 million prescriptions were issued in the UK. *Paroxetine* (seroxat) is another – 4.5 million prescriptions were issued. Another is Lustral (*sertraline*). Indications include phobic anxiety states, OCD, depression and bulimia. They can have unpleasant side effects such as nausea giddiness, insomnia and interference with sexual responses such as anorgasmia. They are said to be non-addictive, but many patients suffer unpleasant withdrawal symptoms. An alleged serious side effect is that of suicidal ideation. It is possible that SSRIs convert a retarded depression into an agitated one with unfortunate effects.

Their use has to be carefully monitored. It is possible that long term effects may include degranulation of the synapses of the neurones, with loss of the higher critical and analytical functions of the brain. Happy but goofy.

16 V.S.A Volatile Substance Abuse.(Glue sniffing)

This is a down-market juvenile habit, often associated with social deprivation, which most children grow out of by the time they are 18. The commonly used substances include benzene, petrol, toluene, butane, and those products containing them such as paint strippers, nail varnish removers, cigarette lighter fuel, contact adhesives. It is usually a group activity, such as are many drug activities, conducted in a park or derelict building, but often solitarily with a sudden change in mental state – intoxication, but possibly leading to delirium, hallucinations and delusions.

Between 1985 and 1991 there were 775 deaths associated with VSA, mainly in Tyne and Wear and Lothian. There were few in Cornwall, and in the Shetland Isles, there were none. The mortality peaked in 1990 at 152 per year, and has been declining since, but there are still 75 per year in the UK. Death occurs from direct toxicity, inhalation of vomit, or explosion if someone lights a match. Legal action has been taken to prevent sellers of the substances selling them to minors.

Unfortunately, doctors, particularly anaesthetists, sometimes become intoxicated by their own vapours, and disciplinary action has to be taken.

CHAPTER SIX

PSYCHO-SURGERY

A *Trepan* is a cylindrical saw. *Trepanning* is the use made of this in boring a hole in the skull. A *Trephine* has a central locating spike. Archaeological evidence has shown that trepanning was used in the Neolithic period (10,000-2000 BC), as skulls with holes bored in them, 1-2 inches in diameter, have been found at burial sites. The indication for this procedure (letting out the devils) remains uncertain, perhaps a cure for epilepsy or 'possession by devils' (probably schizophrenia). Some must have survived as evidence of healing has been found, but for most, the outcome was almost certainly death, from haemorrhage or infection. It may well still be done in very primitive tribes, but the practice is dying out.

Lobotomy – Prefrontal leucotomy

In 1935, at the age of 61, **Antonio Egas Moniz**, a Portuguese psychiatrist, went to meeting of neurologists in London when a pair of researchers, **Carlyle Jackson** and **John Fulton** described the effect of division of a tract of nerve fibres linking the limbic system to the frontal lobes of a female chimpanzee named Becky who had a serious behaviour disorder, screaming, urinating, rejecting food and water. When she awoke she appeared quiet and peaceful. Moniz is supposed to have remarked 'why would it not be feasible to relieve anxiety states in Man by Surgical means? People were shocked at his suggestion. Moniz returned to Portugal, and sought a technique using cadavers in order to carry out a similar procedure in certain chronically disordered patients in the mental hospital.

The first patient was Mrs. M. aged 63. She was anxious and depressed with paranoid features, believing the police were trying to poison her. She had been in the Manicome Bombarda Asylum four and a half years. She was transferred to the neurology service of the Santa Marta Hospital. Under local anaesthetic two holes were drilled on either side of her skull and alcohol was injected into the appropriate area. Moniz had earlier pioneered a technique of cerebral angiography so he was familiar with the anatomy of the brain. Four hours after surgery Moniz questioned her and found some residual cognitive decline. Two months later she was found to be calm, with no anxiety, and with insight into her situation and an absence of paranoid features. Unfortunately, there was no further follow up so the long term consequences remain uncertain. A story heard only too frequently in psychiatric patients.

Moniz wrote 'I recognize that the method could be harmless, and capable of benefiting the insane.'

He first used alcohol, then a special knife called a leucotome. Of the original 20 cases he claimed a complete cure for 7, partial cure for another 7, and 6 who were unhelped.

He published his findings in the American Journal of Psychiatry in 1937. Two surgeons, **Walter Freeman** and **James Watts** developed a technique using a transorbital approach, and restricted the procedure to patients suffering from anxiety and depression, and had findings similar to Moniz. But there were some who became meek and childlike. 'Lobotomy patients may make good citizens' wrote Freeman.

The main problem with it is an ethical one. What constitutes informed consent? It breaches the Golden Rule of Surgery 'Thou shalt not remove or destroy Physiological Tissue.' But there were many testimonials from grateful patients who claimed their lives had been transformed.

But there was said to be a 50% chance of developing epilepsy after leucotomy as scar tissue developed.

In 1949 Moniz was awarded the Nobel prize for Physiology.

Between 1936 and 1978 an estimated 35,000 operations were performed in the USA. President Kennedy's sister Rosemary was operated on, for reasons which remain obscure.

A case is described by **G. Rylander** (1950). She was a Salvation Army worker, a very high-ranking officer. She married a Clergyman. For years she lay in Hospital, constantly complaining that she had committed sins against the Holy Ghost (probably masturbation). She complained of it for weeks and months and her poor husband did his best to distract her, but without success. Then we decided to operate on her....After the dressing had been taken off, I asked her – 'How are you now? What about the Holy Ghost?' Smiling, she answered – 'Oh, the Holy Ghost; there is no Holy Ghost'. Obsessional ruminations can be abolished when all else has failed.

In 1953, Dr **Scoville**, a surgeon from Hartford Connecticut, who had performed over 300 lobotomues, considered by some to be 'reckless', operated on a patient with severe epilepsy, almost status epilepticus. He believed that the cause of the trouble lay in the *hippocampus*, a region deep in the brain that at the time did not seem to serve any useful function. Following surgical removal of the hippocampus, his epilepsy was improved but he had totally lost his ability to retain short term memory. Five minutes after being told something, or being introduced to someone, he was completely unable to recall it. But he did remember long term memories, such as where he lived. Perhaps the hippocampus is the computer analogue of the central processing unit.

With the development of scanning, our knowledge of the structure and function of the brain has improved immeasurably. Computer Axial Tomography (CATSCAN) was introduced in the early 1970's by Dr **Geoffrey Hounsfield**, an English physicist. In this, a narrow band of X-rays is directed at the brain from various angles and the intensity of the radiation after traversing the brain is detected by scintillation recorders. The results are fed into a computer and a picture of the internal structure is revealed.

In the early 1980's this was supplanted by *Magnetic Resonance Imaging* (MRI). In this the patient is placed in a tunnel in which a very strong magnetic field is generated by a supercooled magnet. Pulses of radiofrequency energy are directed at the structure to be analysed. These are absorbed by the hydrogen atoms (protons) of water in the tissues, the axes of rotation of which have been deflected by the magnetic field and energy is absorbed. With precession, energy is emitted at a different frequency which can be detected by a receiver and its intensity gives a measure of the density of the structure under examination. This is analysed by a computer and a remarkably good picture is obtained. It is safer than a Catscan as it does not involve ionizing radiation, but is very much more expensive. An MRI scanner cost £750,000 in 1990.

In addition to our knowledge of the structure of the brain, knowledge of its function has been investigated by *Positron Emission Tomography* (PET scan). In this, a solution of glucose labeled with a short-lived positron-emitting radioactive isotope such as C^{11} or N^{13} is injected into a vein and its uptake measured with a scintillation counter, as the positrons capture an electron and emit gamma-rays. This gives an indication of the glucose uptake of the region under investigation and hence its function.

With knowledge of the internal structure of the brain these led to the development of stereotactic surgery.

Much of the uncertainty has been removed from brain surgery. With the rise in effective medication for depressive disorders there was a falling off of the procedure in the 1950's and by 1970 only 20 operations were performed that year in the USA, mainly focusing on the limbic system the cingulate gyrus and the amygdala, and the indication – Obsessive Compulsive Disorder (OCD). It was later declared illegal in California and Oregon and Russia.

In the UK in 1974 158 leucotomies were performed, In 1976 only 119. The concensus is that it should only be done if several years of conventional treatment have failed.

CHAPTER SEVEN

INTERSEX

NOTE: The word 'Sex' has changed its usage and meaning in the last few years. Historically and scientifically, it means the differentiation between male and female. Nowadays it is used as a pronoun and means sexual intercourse or copulation, or even sodomy (anal intercourse) or fellatio (oral intercourse) such as in 'Did you have sex last night?'. The word 'Gender' describes masculinity or femininity, the non-physical component of the personality. Also it has been used to differentiate Proper Nouns grammatically in the Latin languages such as French, Spanish and German. The English language does not have grammatical gender as it is felt to be pointless.

Here, the words will be used in their original or historic meaning.

Biological (genetic) sex determination.

Glossary
A *chromosome* that is not a sex chromosome is called an *autosome*.
Karyotype is the number, size and shape of the chromosomes in the cell.
Genotype is the genetic constitution of an individual.
Phenotype is the appearance of an individual, resulting from the effects of both genes and environment.

In Man, there are 44 autosomes (22x2 alleles or allelomorphs) and two sex chromosomes denoted X and Y in the body (somatic) cells, as distinct from the germ cells or sex cells produced in the testes (spermatozoa) or ovaries (ova).

In the female (ovum), the genetic structure or karyotype is 22X.

In the male, spermatozoa are of two types, one, 22X, carrying the X female determining chromosome, the other 22Y carrying the Y male determining chromosome. At fertilisation, the male and female gametes fuse, making the normal female karyotype 46XX and the male, 46XY.

The presence of both an ovary and a testis in a single individual is called *hermaphroditism* and occurs in earthworms but not in mammals. But there is a very rare condition in Man in which non-functioning remnants occur - (see below).

However, there are varieties of pseudo-hermaphroditism that do occur in Man, in which virilism of female genitals and feminization of male genitals occurs. These are due to abnormal sex hormones circulating in utero. In cows, a *freemartin* is a classic intersex, in which circulating androgens in utero cause masculinization of a genetically female individual, when there are twins, one male, one female.

The classical case of what was probably pseudo-hermaphroditism was that of Dr **James Barry** (1795-1875) who functioned superbly well as an army surgeon and was only found to be female at post-mortem (see below).

The perception of sexual identity (masculine or feminine) sometimes goes wrong and the affected individual feels, with absolute conviction, irrational though it may be, that he or she is in the wrong body. This is the true *transsexual,* a term popularised by Dr **Harry Benjamin** of New York, in the 1950s. This is also called *gender dysphoria*. In 2004 a bill was introduced into Parliament to give legal recognition to this- The Gender Recognition Bill (gerbil).

The question of sexual orientation and its origin is a difficult one, and there are no clear answers. From birth most children are aware of differences, and observation of animal behaviour creates an interest. Problems arise at puberty, about ages 10-12 in Western society, though this is falling. A stage of homosexual attachment is common at this time (crushes or infatuations), but most grow out of it. It is possible that a firm attachment, possibly due to physical or genital contact, to an older man or woman may arrest normal physiological development.

Another possibility as to causation is that there may be some noxious substance (oestrogenic) in the water supply which may provoke homosexuality. Another possibility is that there is a genetic element.

'Homosexuality is assuredly no advantage, but it is nothing to be ashamed of, no vice, no degradation, it cannot be classified as an illness; we consider it to be a variation of the sexual function, produced by a certain arrest of the sexual development. It is a great injustice to persecute homosexuality as a crime – and a cruelty too.' **Sigmund Freud**.

There is often considerable promiscuity, many partners, in male homosexuals, which greatly increases the likely consequence of sexually transmitted disease occurring, gonorrhea, non-specific urethritis (Chlamidia), syphilis, AIDS, and Hepatitis B as well as infertility in the female.

Many societies regard homosexuality with great distaste. In England it was illegal until about 1960 with great suffering for those afflicted, and opportunities for blackmail. Those found 'guilty' were referred by the courts for 'treatment' as it was considered a 'disease'. One of the 'treatments' was 'aversion', consisting of 'patients' been shown pictures of homosexual activity accompanied by an electric shock, or some other such unpleasant experience. Another 'treatment' was circumcision. The success rate of these procedures was zero and the suicide rate approached 30%. The computer scientist Alan Turing, famous for his work at Bletchley Park during World War II in cracking the German Enigma code, saving many lives in the Battle of the North Atlantic, was a victim of this. He ate an apple, containing cyanide.

In 1968 Homosexuality was deleted from the 2nd edition of the Diagnostic and Statistical Manual of Mental Disorders (DSM 2) as it was no longer considered a disease.

In 2001 the Association of Psychiatrists of China declared that homosexuality was no longer a mental illness, thereby excusing themselves from having cases referred to them for 'treatment'.

Transvestism is a behaviour disorder in which the person, usually male, obtains a thrill (usually sexual) by dressing as the opposite sex – cross dressing, to the annoyance of the wife and dismay and humiliation of the children. Some seek a living as entertainers; some people consider this hilarious, others merely ludicrous. But women dressed as men are considered neither hilarious nor ludicrous.

But homosexuality even occurs in insects. Two male dragon-flies have been observed mating. It is, however, a biological mistake, a dead-end, as there is no possibility of reproduction.

A new terminology has arisen for people who identify themselves with transsexualism – *transpeople*. Transmen are those who are assigned as female at birth but feel they are in fact male. Transwomen those who are assigned as male at birth but feel themselves to be female.

Half of male to female transsexuals identify as lesbian (comfortable with women) while most female to male transsexuals identify as heterosexual.

Problems have arisen owing to different tax liabilities of single people as to married couples, particularly with death duties now called inheritance tax. Homosexuals living in stable relationships (2 years and over 18) can have a short birth certificates issued to permit marriage following a legal judgement from the European Court of Justice in 1998, and in the UK the Gender Recognition Act was passed in 2004. This presumably would allow one of a couple to bequeath their property to the other free of Inheritance Tax in the UK. The sensible thing to do to avoid these conundrums would be to abolish inheritance tax.

But there are many variations and uncertainties in sexuality, which makes it so interesting. Clearly, the objective of it all is reproduction. There was the curious case of the Olympic hurdler Maria Patino, who, having won a medal, was stripped of her award and humiliated when it was discovered that she was genetically XY. However, after a 3 year battle for justice, she was vindicated and sex tests were withdrawn.

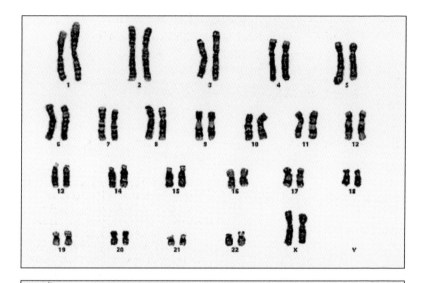

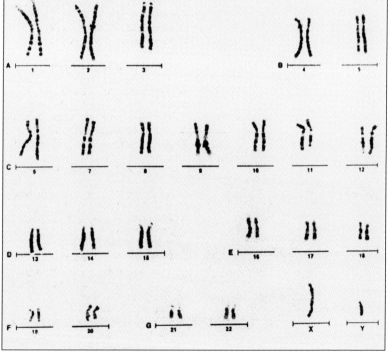

Karyograms of the human female (top) and male chromosomes.

DISORDERS OF SEXUAL DIFFERENTIATION

Karyotype	Phenotype.
1. Turner's syndrome. 45 X Single X chromosome	Female. Ovarian agenesis. Absence of secondary sex characters. Short stature, web neck, coarctation of aorta. Low IQ
2. Androgen Insensitivity Syndrome 46 XY	(A.I.S.) Also called pseudo-hermaphroditism or testicular feminisation. Genetically male, but appear to be female at birth, as the target organs have not responded to circulating androgens. Have a rudimentary vagina but no uterus. Often present as a hernia at the age of 1 and are found to have small and undescended testes which are generally removed to prevent malignant change. Patients are reared as female. Inherited through the female. A 1-in-4 chance of developing the syndrome if mother is a carrier of the genetic defect. General advice is to rear the child as female and construct a vagina after puberty
3. Congenital Adrenal Hyperplasia. 46 XX	Also called pseudo-hermaphroditism. Genetically female. Due to excessive adrenal masculinising hormones in utero. Appear to be male at birth as the clitoris is enlarged and appears to be a penis. Uterus and ovaries are present, but no vagina. In the past clitoridectomy was performed but this meant sexual response was impaired. Present attitude is to delay any operation.
4. Kleinefelter's Syndrome. 47 XXY.	Incidence – 1:500. Born to older mothers (>40) similar to Down's Syndrome, possibly due to non-disjunction of the X chromosome in meiosis in the ovary. Have small testes, appear to be male, but have gynaecomastia. Most live as men but some are more comfortable as a female. May be obese and diabetic. If female orientation, a vagina may be constructed. .
5. True hermaphroditism. 46 XX/XY or mosaic	Very rare. Male or indeterminate sexuality at birth, have rudimentary ovaries and testes, which are usually removed to reduce the risk of malignancy. If raised as female, later operation to construct vagina.may be possible.

CHAPTER EIGHT

PSYCHIATRY, POLITICS AND THE LAW

The Mental Health Act of 1959 repealed all previous legislation on Mental Disorder in the UK. Abolished were terms like mental deficiency, mental defective, idiot, imbecile, feeble minded, and moral defective. The Term Psychiatric Hospital was substituted for Mental Hospital and Hospital for the Mentally Subnormal.

Four categories of mentally disordered patients were recognised.

1. Mental illness.
2. Severe subnormality.
3. Subnormality.
4. Psychopathic disorder.

Severe subnormality means a state of arrested development of mind so severe that the patient is incapable of leading an independent life or of guarding himself against serious exploitation or, in the case of a child, that he will be incapable to this degree when an adult.

Subnormality refers to a state of arrested or incomplete development of mind which includes subnormaltiy of the intelligence. Such a patient requires special care or training but the arrested development of mind does not amount to severe subnormality.

Psychopathic disorder means a persistent disorder or disability of mind whether or not including subnormality of the intelligence, which results in abnormally aggressive irresponsible conduct on the part of the patient and requires or is susceptible to medical treatment or to care or training under medical supervision.

The aim of the Act is to separate the subnormal from the severely subnormal patients and to treat the former either in separate units or in association with patients suffering from certain types of mental illness. The severely subnormal need special hospital care to meet their particular needs.

Psychopathic patients may be treated in separate units or in hospital in association with the subnormal or with the mentally ill.

The centres provided by local health authorities for the occupation or training of mentally subnormal patients are now referred to as Training Centres, in the case of children, and in the case of adults, Training Centres or Occupational Centres, depending on what they do.

This Act abolished the procedure of Certification and Detention by judicial authority.

Under the Act patients are admitted either informally (voluntarily), or compulsorily, under the following arrangements.

1. Section 25 Admission for observation. Duration 28 days.
2. Section 29 Emergency admission for observation. Duration 72 hours.
3. Section 26 Admission for Treatment. Duration 1 year in first instance.
4. Section 60,61,67. Admission on Court Order.

Compulsory admission has to be based, under Section 25 and Section 26, on the written recommendation of two medical practitioners, by the nearest relative or a local authority social worker, to the managers of the hospital to which admission is sought. A similar procedure applies under section 33 for application for guardianship. One of the doctors has to be specially approved for the purpose by the local heath authority, the other the patient's GP. Under section 29, an urgent application can be made by any relative or social worker, supported by one medical recommendation.

An appeal may be lodged against compulsory detention within 6 months of admission, by the nearest relative or the patient, to a Mental Health Review Tribunal.

The Court of Protection has been established to deal with the property of those compulsorily detained. The Court appoints a receiver who acts on behalf of the patient. This is mostly used in the case of the elderly confused. Often a Power of Attorney has been established to render the above unnecessary.(It is quite expensive)

Criminal Responsibility
From the legal point of view, responsibility means liability for punishment.

The defence may plead unsoundness of mind for any criminal charge, but usually for murder.

In 1843 McNaghten shot and killed Sir Robert Peel's secretary. It was shown that McNaghten had suffered from delusions of persecution and that the killing had been inspired by these delusions. The Judge directed the jury to find him not guilty. There was great public interest in the case, culminating in a debate in the House of Lord when the famous Mcnaghten Rules were formulated.

The rules state that, in order to establish a defence on the ground of insanity, it must be proved:

1. that, at the time of the offence, the accused was labouring under such a defect of reason from disease of the mind as not to know the nature and quality of the act he was doing or, if he did know what he was doing, he did not know that it was wrong.
2. If the accused commits an act by reason of delusion, the degree of responsibility is based on the justification which the delusion would provide if it were true.

These rules were regarded by many doctors as absurd, and thus it was left to the jury to decide insanity and to pronouce the verdict. At the time, the death penalty was applied for murder, and no doubt juries took this into account in reaching their verdict.

In 1957, the Homicide Act introduced the concept of diminished responsibility. This states that when a person kills or is party to a killing, he should not be convicted of murder if he was suffering from such an abnormality of the mind(whether arising from a condition of arrested or retarded development of mind or any inherent causes or induced by disease or injury) as substantially impaired his mental responsibility for his acts and admissions in doing or being a party to the killing. If these circumstances apply, the verdict is Manslaughter not Murder.

— • —

Politics

"A ruling group is a ruling group so long as it can nominate its successors. It is only concerned with perpetuating itself. Oligarchal rule needs the perception of a world view and way of life imposed by the

*dead upon the living. Who wields power is not important providing
the hierarchical structure remains the same."*

(George Orwell -*1984)*

The supreme virtue of democracy is that it introduces the possibility of
change – in a word – evolution – of the social structures. The alternative is
revolution, with its appalling destruction.

Numerous attempts have been made to classify people- 'The
Psychological Profiles' of Jung. But there is a natural one, the 'dominance
heirarchy' or peck order, found in social animals such as pigs, and chickens, chimpanzees. The smallest pig, the runt of the litter, has to develop a
craftiness and agility in order to survive being pushed out by his larger
more powerful brothers and sisters. The smallest hen often gets pecked to
death by larger birds. In lions, there is a dominant male who copulates with
the females. In wolves, the dominant female is the one who has cubs. In
Frazer's Golden Bough, the dominant Priest is displaced (killed) when a
more powerful one can assume the position.

Hippocrates (b. 460BC) – the Father of Medicine – who introduced
rationality and an ethical basis to medical practice, classified people into
four types. The Sanguine, who becomes Choleric under stress, the
Phlegmatic, who becomes Melancholic under stress.

*Man cannot and should not try to exist without some form of religion,
but, let us add, that although it is quite possible to indoctrinate people with ideas based on an out-of-date economic or historical tradi-
tion, or even on deliberate lies, and keep them fixed on these beliefs,
a nation's health and efficiency depends on a close relation between
social practice and religious belief. Any contradiction between them
can only help to breed mental stress and impair judgment. No alternative exists to Christianity in the Western world, but it will probably
become necessary to put the incidents of the New Testament into less
ambiguous historical perspective; consolidate Christ's sacrifice for
the sins of His people; reinforce the prime texts of 'fear God' and
'Love they neighbour as thyself'; give these real social and political
validity; and thus make it unnecessary for the businessman, or
labourer, or priest to be the victim of a dissociation between his acts
and his profession."*

Yet science, however exploited by soldiers, merchants and politi-

cians, is often a negative discipline; religion, ethics and politics should be strongly positive ones."

Though men are not dogs, they should humbly try to remember how much they resemble dogs in their brain functions, and not boast themselves as demigods. They are gifted with religious and social apprehensions, and they are gifted with the power of reason; but all these faculties are physiologically entailed to the brain. Therefore the brain should not be abused by having forced upon it any religious or political mystique (or drugs for that matter) that stunts the reason, or any form of crude rationalism that stunts the religious sense.

(Sargant)

The basic instincts of the higher animals, including Man, are to create, to communicate, to belong and to explore. Religion in Man is necessary to satisfy the need to belong, in a spiritual environment.

EPILOGUE I

𝔜et man is born unto trouble, as the sparks fly upward.

The Book of Job, Chapter 5 verse 7

Nil Carborundum Illegitimos

*'Don't Let the Bastards Grind You Down'

EPILOGUE II

APPENDIX 1

A note on the Anatomy and Physiology of the Central Nervous System.

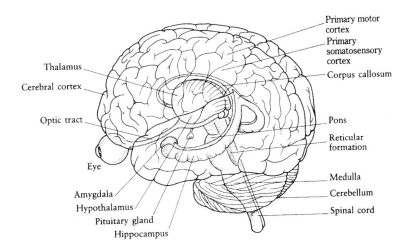

Anatomy

The brain and spinal cord are covered by three layers of the *meninges*.The outer hard sheath is the *dura mater*. Beneath that is the *arachnoid mater* a spider's web like layer, and beneath that is the vascular *pia mater*. The spinal cord usually ends at the level of the upper border of the second lumbar vertebra: lower down is the *spinal theca*, containing nerve roots and Cerebro-Spinal Fluid. The CSF is produced in a vascular layer inside the lateral ventricles of the brain. From there, it flows through the foramen of Munro into the third ventricle. Then via the aqueduct of Sylvius into the fourth ventricle, then out of the lateral recesses of the fourth ventricle into the subarachnoid space and over the brain. *Lumbar puncture* (*spinal tap* in the USA) is usually performed by inserting a fine needle into the spinal theca at the level between the second and third lumbar vertebrae. The CSF is a clear colourless liquid (normally gin-clear). If it is blood-stained, this can indicate trauma of needle insertion, or sub-arachnoid haemorrage. If it is cloudy, this indicates infection, as it is full of leucocytes – meningitis.

The basic unit of the nervous system is the *neurone*. There are about 1.5 x 10^9 neurones in the brain at birth. They are said to diminish at the rate of

2000 per day subsequently. The head and the brain grow up to the age of 7. The brain continues to develop with increasing myelinisation of the axons, particularly of the prefrontal cortex, until after puberty. The neurones are highly specialised nucleated cells from 10-50μ in diameter, with a long projection called an *axon*, and many short projections called *dendrites*. These projections interact with other cells at a junction called a *synapse*,(a term introduced by Sir **William Sherrington**, author of 'The 'Integrative Action of the Nervous System') but do not touch, leaving an interval of 10-20 nanometres. Synapses can be either excitatory or inhibitory. It has been estimated that there may be 10,000 synaptic contacts on the dendrites of the Purkinje cells of the cerebellum. Axons are covered with a fatty sheath of *myelin*, which acts as an insulator. Other brain cells are astrocytes, stellate, meso-striatal (found in the substantia nigra of the brain stem,) and neuroglia, supporting cells.

The grey matter of the cortex is the principal site of neurones. Specialised neurones in the cortex dedicated to movement are called upper motor neurones and their axons descend into the spinal cord to connect with the lower motor neurones in the cord. Axons from the latter innervate the muscles and terminate at the motor end-plate. Voluntary muscle is striated, with transverse bands. Involuntary muscle does not have these bands, it is called smooth muscle. Heart muscle is a syncytium, with branched interlocking fibres, and will contract provided it is stretched.

Likewise, axons from sensory cells located in the dorsal root ganglia of the spinal cord descend to their respective sensors, touch, heat, pain, etc. and nerve impulses travel upwards in the spinal cord to reach the brain where they interact with sensory neurones in the brain.

Attempts have been made to localise various functions of the brain. Thus, the visual cortex is located at the back of the brain. The auditory cortex is in the medial aspect of the lateral lobe of the brain on the left in right handed people, on the right in left handed people. Broca's area, devoted to speech, is located in the auditory cortex. The 'body image', inverted, is located on the surface of the sensory cortex. This remains even when a limb has been amputated, giving ride to the distressing phenomenon of 'phantom limb', the perception that a limb is still present when it isn't.

The *limbic system* consists of the hippocampus, the thalamus, the hypothalamus, the amygdala, septum, fornix and cingulate gyrus of the cerebral cortex.(see diagram above). It is thought to be associated with emotions and short term memory. The hippocampus in Man is a structure about 5 cm. Long situated beneath the lateral ventricle.

MRI scanning at birth has revealed that some babies are born without a corpus callosum, a thick tract of nerve fibres that link the two cerebral hemispheres – acallosal. Surprisingly little disability results, except that a raised intracranial pressure necessitates the insertion of a shunt to drain the CSF into the peritoneum. Perhaps there is something to be said for routine brain scanning in all premature babies to exclude conditions such as anencephaly (no cortex) which would be incompatible with independent existence, to prevent futile attempts at resuscitation.

There are so many interconnecting links that other tracts can take over damaged ones, such as may be the case in *strokes* – cerebral thrombosis, haemorrhage, or embolism.

Physiology

The membranes of all cells are polarised, and in nerve cells are electrically excitable. There is an excess of potassium and a deficiency of sodium and calcium within the cell compared with the interstitial fluid. There is an ionic 'pump' within the cell in order to maintain this gradient, and energy derived from glucose metabolism is needed, via adenosine triphosphate (ATP). Thus there is a membrane potential of minus 60 millivolts within the cell.*

FOOTNOTE

*The cell membrane consists of a double layer of *phospholid*. This is based on the 3-carbon chain glycerol (glycerine - a tri-atomic alcohol - tri-hydroxy-propane). Its 3 carbon atoms are labelled Sn1, Sn2 and Sn3. Fatty acids are attached to Sn1 and Sn2 but at Sn3 there is a phosphorus atom, to which are attached four possible molecules - choline, inositol, serine and ethanolamine, called head groups, are water soluble and hydrophilic. The other end, Sn1 & 2, containing the fatty acids are water-insoluble. Thus, when put into water phospholipids form a double layer, the water soluble ends forming the outer membrane, the fats forming the core or inner layer. When the phospholipids form a tube, there will be a central channel containing water which will conduct electricity. This is the basis of the nerve fibre. There are protein molecules at intervals along the tube, which break down the insulating properties and permit impulses to pass.

The brain consists mostly of phospholipids, with 60-70% being fatty acids, especially highly unsaturated fatty acids, especially in the Sn2 position. (Saturated fats have no double bonds and are solid at room temperature; unsaturated fats have several double bonds, a deficit of hydrogen atoms, and are liquid.) Two essential fatty acids – they must be in the food intake as they cannot be synthesised in the body, are known:- linoleic acid (LA).and alpha -linolinic acid (ALA) These compounds are inactive and are converted to active compounds of which the most important is Arachidonic Acid,(AA) a 20 carbon chain with 4 double bonds, which makes up 8% of the dry matter of the brain, and Eicosipentaenoic Acid,(EPA) and Docosahexaenoic Acid (DHA) which are also active. The presence of saturated fats in the diet can slow down these transformations, so it is important to reduce these in the diet. Human milk contains AA, EPA and DHA so the baby gets its important compounds directly. Most animal milks contain only LA and ALA. Hopefully AA, EPA and DHA will now be added to 'formula' milk. These latter fatty acids are found in meat and aquatic plants such as micro-algae, the latter being the base of the food chain for fish.

It is postulated that during a febrile episode large amounts of AA are released from the phospholipids, and activate prostaglandins which are responsible for the mobilisation of the anti-inflammatory response. This AA improves brain activity to such an extent that the symptoms of schizophrenia remit, only to relapse when the temperature falls. Likewise, a fish oil, Kirunal, containing 25% EPA in a dose of 8 Gms per day, has been shown to improve the symptoms of schizophrenia.

When a stimulus arrives via the synapse, the membrane rapidly becomes permeable, depolarises and the cell develops a positive potential within it of +30 millivolts, occurring over 750 microseconds. Almost as rapidly, the membrane repolarises. But there is a refractory period of 1-2 milliseconds, when the neurone will not respond. When the neurone 'fires', an 'action potential' descends down the axon to effect the necessary activity. This is an 'all or none' response; consequently, nerve impulses are 'digital', a series of ones and zeros similar to binary logic in computers.

Both nerve transmission and muscular contraction are essentially similar to the release experienced when a stretched elastic band is released. Energy is expended in stretching the band, similar to polarizing the nerve cell and expanding the muscle fibre, and released when it 'fires' or the muscle contracts. This probably explains the phenomenon of rigor mortis, rigidity of the body several hours after death.

Various neurotransmitter chemicals are released at the synapse, glutamate is the principal excitatory one in the brain. The principal inhibitory neurotransmitter is *GABA, g amino-butyric acid*. Another neurotransmitter is *acetyl-choline*, and blockage of this, such as with the muscle relaxant scoline, or the Amazon Indians' *curare*, causes paralysis. *5-hydroxy-tryptamine (serotonin)* is another, as are *dopamine* (synthesised in the body from *tyramine*) and *nor-adrenalin*. (*nor-epinephrine* in the USA).

In Parkinson's disease, there is degeneration of the substantia nigra in the brain stem, and reduction of dopamine levels in the basal ganglia. (corpus striatum, putamen and globus pallidus.) If the reduction amounts to 80%, Parkinson's disease occurs. Administration of dopamine does not help as it does not cross the blood/brain barrier. But L-DOPA (di-hydroxy-phenylalanine) does and is converted to dopamine in the brain, and in doses of 1 gram per day is effective in relieving the distressing symptoms of the disease – which are principally, tremor, muscle rigidity, leading to partial paralysis.

Amphetamine causes release of dopamine at nerve ending stores, as does noradrenaline and serotonin and can induce a state resembling paranoid schizophrenia in high doses in humans.

The anti-psychotics block the dopamine receptors, and this could be the basis of their effectiveness in schizophrenia.

In Alzheimers disease, there is loss of neurones in the cerebral cortex and cholinegic neurones in the hippocampus. This structure is thought to be important in short-term memory and the amygdala in emotional responses.

The biochemistry of depression came to light as a serendipitous effect of the anti-tuberculous drug isoniazid. With the discovery of streptomycin as a cure for tuberculosis in the 1940s it was found that the organism rapidly developed resistance to the anti-biotic. So it became necessary to add p-amino salicylic acid and isoniazid, both weak anti-tuberculous agents, to prevent this. Patients on isoniazid experienced a marked mood elevation and this was found to be due to their ability to nhibit the enzyme Mono-Amine Oxidase. So a series of Mono-amine-oxidase-inhibitors (MAOIs) was developed and marketed as anti-depressants.

Unfortunately, there was an unacceptable side effect in that they caused a marked and dangerous rise of blood-pressure, in some patients, leading to strokes. This was particularly after consumption of cheese containing the amino-acid tyramine.(Especially blue cheeses) Additionally, a very distressing side effect is *tardive dyskinesia*, a condition similar to Parkinson's disease (extra-pyramidal syndrome) characterised by tremor, rigidity and involuntary movements, symptoms which may persist in spite of withdrawal of the drug. This condition may occur after anti-psychotic drugs especially phenothiazines, such as chlorpromazine, in high doses.

Search for substances that increased the levels of serotonin (5-hydroxytryptamine) and nor-adrenaline in the synapse led to the development of the present anti-depressants, Selective Serotonin Reuptake Inhibitors - SSRIs, such as Prozac and Seroxat. These may take a week or two to become effective.

Many sedatives and anti-depressants have untoward side effects. Patients may develop tolerance, requiring increasing doses, and dependence. Unpleasant withdrawal symptoms such as insomnia and panic attack may occur. To prevent these, patients must be closely monitored and treatment should be restricted to short term use, preferably less than 4 weeks, with slow reduction. Some animal experiments show that these substances hinder appropriate response to stressful situations, happy but goofy.

Autonomic Nervous System (Involuntary)
The functional division of the nervous system which supplies the glands, heart, and smooth muscle.

This is divided into the Sympathetic and the Parasympathetic Systems.

1. Sympathetic. This arises from the thoracic and lumbar regions of the spinal cord.

2. The Parasympathetic arises from the mid-brain, hind-brain and sacral regions of the spinal cord.

APPENDIX 2

Table of admissions to Bethlem 1772-1787.
(From *300 years of Psychiatry* -Hunter & McAlpine)

Ages			Reasons for admission	
>10	1			
10-20	132		Misfortune, troubles, disappointments, grief	206
20-30	813		Religion and Methodism	90*
30-40	908		Love	74
40-50	652		Jealousy	9
50-60	266		Pride	8
60+	78		Study	15
			Fright	58
Mischievous		743	Drink and Intoxication	110
Not mischievous		886	Fevers	72
Attempted suicide		323	Obstruction	10
Committed murders			Family and Hereditary	115
upwords		20	Contusions and fractures of skull	12
			Venereal	14
			Small pox	7
			Ulcers and scab dried up	5

Of the cured	924	*John Wesley was forbidden entry to Bethlem.
Incurable	1694	
Relapses	535	
Deaths	250	

— • —

Table of Admissions to Maison Royale de Charenton 1811-1812.
(from *The Historical Development of British Psychiatry* – Denis Leigh)

Moral Causes		Physical Causes	
Domestic Griefs	89	Hereditary Predisposition	93
Excessive Study and Watching	8	Masturbation	33
Reverses of Fortune	20	Libertinism	24
Passion for Gaming	2	Use of Mercury	16
Jealousy	13	Abuse of Wine	64
Disappointment in Love	21	Insolation	7
Injured self-love	6	Effect of Carbonic acid gas	2
Fright	7	Suppression of Habitual Evacuations	13
Dévotion Exaltée	18	Consequence of parturition	10
Excess of Joy	1	Blows on the Head	4
Total	182		256

A BRIEF HISTORY OF PSYCHIATRY

— • —

Admissions to Mental Hospitals and Mental handicap Hospitals 1962 and 1970
(from *Psychiatry in Dissent* – Anthony Clare)

	1962	**1970**
Section 25 & 29	27, 692	28,403
Section 26	1,858	1,140
Sections 135/6	750	1,439
Other	<u>1,584</u>	<u>1,725</u>
	31, 874 (20%)	32,761 (17%)
Voluntary	<u>124,884 (80%)</u>	<u>161,958 (83%)</u>
Total	156,758	194,719
Resident patients 31 December	197,081	171,051

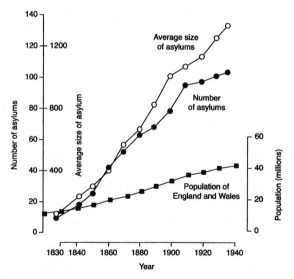

Figure 1 The Asylum Era. Number and average size (places) of County and Borough asylums in England and Wales, 1827-1936. and total population. Data for 1927 are from Jones (1955); the remainder are from the Annual Reports of the Lunacy Commissioners and the Board of Control. From *On the History of Lunacy* by E.H. Hare. Gabbay 1998.

Perhaps this represents the transfer from a primarily agrarian economy to a town and city based industrial one, where behaviour disorder is not so relatively tolerated. If this be the case, the developing counties should take note and not make the mistakes of old.

APPENDIX 3

History of Psychiatry of Exeter

For many years, those suffering from thought disorder, communication dis-order or behaviour disorder (social rejects) were regarded as 'possessed by devils' and priests were summoned to exorcise the devils. There was much cruelty and a high mortality, witches being burnt at the stake. The monas-teries provided sanctuary for some, until they were dissolved by Henry VIII about 1535.

The first Mental Hospital in Exeter was St. Thomas' Hospital for Lunatics at Bowhill House, Exeter, which stemmed from a bequest of £200 in 1795 by a Mr. Pitfield. It was expressly intended to provide treatment for middle class and professional people not dependent on the rates.

In the same year, the Bishop of Exeter, invited the Revd James Manning, a nonconformist minister, to dinner at the Bishop's Palace. The Bishop said 'I have £200 to give away' and suggested he give it to the Devon and Exeter Hospital. Revd Manning replied that the Hospital had no need of funds (the rules of the Hospital expressly forbade the admission of lunatics) but that he had £200 at his command, and put forward a proposal for a lunatic asylum. The Bishop agreed to write to the Grand Jury of Devon for approval, which was given, and funds started to pour in

On March 29th, 1803, the foundation stone was laid by Revd Manning. He reminded those present of the miserable plight of lunatics.

> 'Cut off from all the relations and charities of life, the poor lunatic is dead to every gentle sympathy which God hath ordained to make our journey through this world easy and comfortable to us.
> In general none of the duties of this life can be properly attended to, and all preparation for another world is wholly suspended.'

The Hospital was built at Dunsford Road, Exeter, with accommodation for 70 patients'. Admission was to be facilitated 'without delay' as it was pointed out that the smallest delay could result in fatal acts of violence.

At the time there was a view that insanity was a hopeless incurable dis-ease and that asylums were, to their unfortunate inmates, prisons, the gates of which death alone would open. The founders were impressed with the fallacy of this opinion, and that, with proper care, four fifths of cases would recover, provided that there was no pre-existing 'weakness of intellect.' Both private and pauper patients were eligible for admission, the latter requiring a certificate signed by a Clergyman or Justice, and the relieving officer of the Parish, together with a medical certificate signed by a physician, surgeon or apothecary. In the case of a private patient, application was made by a friend or relative, and two medical certificates were required. The fees varied from 5 shillings to 3 guineas a week. If the charges were assessed at less than ten and sixpence a week, physicians attended without fees. Patients were reviewed at least once a month. In addition, there was a Medical Superintendent who was answerable to the Visiting Commissioners in Lunacy.

By 1845 there was a Matron, 5 male and 9 female attendants. The average number of patients admitted and discharged annually was 17, and there were up to 8 deaths, mostly from elderly patients.

But during the first half of the nineteenth century the reputation of Insane Asylums was at a low ebb. There was gross neglect, embezzlement of funds and arson, often causing deaths of patients. The conditions at the Bethlem Hospital (Bedlam) were depicted in Hogarth's engravings.

The 1808 Act had authorized the setting up of 16 County Asylums, and in 1842 the Metropolitan Commissioners in Lunacy were given powers to inspect all institutions for the insane, and to report to Parliament.

They visited Bowhill House and recommended more extensive grounds. Twenty acres in the parish of Heavitree were purchased by the Governors. A large loan had to be floated and the public were encouraged to subscribe to the charity. The foundation stone was laid on October 18th, 1866 and Wonford House, with accommodation for 120 patients, was opened by the President, the Earl of Devon, on July 7th, 1869. The sum of £20,000 had been raised but a further £15,000 had to be borrowed.

In the latter half of the19th century, the specialty of psychiatry had developed, with emphasis on treatment over mere custodial care.

BIBLIOGRAPHY

1. The Rise and Fall of Modern Medicine. Le Fanu.Little Brown. 1999
2. Conundrum. Jan Morris Faber and Faber. 1974
3. Autism. Uta Frith Basil Blackwell. 1989.
4. Against Therapy. Jeffrey Masson. William Collins 1989
5. Jung. Deidre Blair. Little Brown 2004
6. The Myth of Irrationality. John McCrone.Carroll & Graf, New York. 1993.
7. Opening Skinner's Box. Lauren Slater. Bloomsbury. 2004.
8. Brain biochemistry and Brain Disorders. Philip G. Strange. OUP. 1992.
9. Freud. Anthony Storr. OUP 1989.
10. The battle for the Mind. William Sargant. Pan (Heinemann) 1959
11. Clinical Medicine. Kumar and Clark. Balliere and Tindall 1994.
12. Cognitive Therapy and the Emotional disorders. Aaron T. Beck Penguin 1976.
13. Matters of Substance. Griffith Edwards. Allen Lane. 2004.
14. Short Textbook of Psychiatry. Linford Rees. Hodder & Stoughton, 1982.
15. 300 years of Psychiatry. Hunter and Mc.Alpine. OUP 1963
16. On the History of Lunacy. E.H.Hare. Gabbay. 1998
17. Psychiatry for the Poor. Hunter and McAlpine. Dawson. 1974.
18. Drink, Drugs and Dependence. Caan and de Belleroche. Routledge 2002
19. Cognitive Analytic Therapy and Borderline Personality Disorder. Anthony Ryle. John Riley & Sons. 1997.
20. A History of Exeter Hospitals, 1170-1948 P.M.G. Russell.
21. A Century of Psychiatry. Ed. Hugh Freeman. Harcourt. London 1999.
22. Psychiatry in Dissent. Anthony Clare.Tavistock 1980
23. The Historical Development of British Psychiatry. Denis Leigh. Pergamon. 1961.
24. The Oxford Illustrated Companion to Medicine. OUP.2001
25. The Madness of Adam and Eve. Horrobin. Corgi. 2002.
26. Oxford Textbook of Psychiatry. Gelder, Gath, Mayou. OUP. 1989.

PERSONAL NAME INDEX

SUBJECT INDEX